First on The Hill

First on The Hill

ATLANTA'S MEDICAL CAMELOT:

The Founding and Early Days of Northside Hospital, and the Rise of a Medical Center

Charles M. Silverstein, M.D.

Longstreet Press
Atlanta, Georgia

Published by
LONGSTREET PRESS, INC.
A subsidiary of Cox Newspapers,
A division of Cox Enterprises, Inc.
2140 Newmarket Parkway, Suite 118
Marietta, GA 30067

Printed in the United States of America
First printing 1993
ISBN 1-56352-143-1

Color separations by American Color, Atlanta, GA

Book design and production by Fine Print Typography, Inc.

"Don't let it be forgot
that once there was a spot
for one brief, shining moment
that was known as Camelot."

LERNER AND LOEWE'S *Camelot*

Camelot (kam´a lot´), *n.* **1.** the legendary site
of King Arthur's palace and court, possibly
near Exeter, England. **2.** any idyllic site or period.

Contents

APPENDICIES

First on The Hill

Preface

In this world of ceaseless change and too-selective memory, we all have the need to know ourselves, our roots, as well as our wants. Three years ago, Donald Hutton, Northside's third administrator, asked me to write this history. He knew I had been involved with the hospital since its conception, had chronicled its early times before, and was approaching retirement.

After I finally agreed, my oldest friend, an ex-newspaper editor, chided: "Why are you doing this? If you do it right, and you will, it will take more time and effort than you realize. And if you tell it like it was, which you will, you may make some folks less than pleased."

This account, which has somehow expanded into a book, is my gift to Northside Hospital and to The Hill, with the hope that it will be useful. It is dedicated, with affection and deep appreciation, to all those physicians and other health workers, business people and other community leaders, neighbors and friends who joined together early on to make a cherished maxim of my youth — "It is remarkable what you can accomplish if you are not concerned about who gets the credit" — come true.

As I thought about it later, there were several reasons for my writing this. First, in the past five years of Northside's 23 years as a hospital, I was often struck by the fact that most members of the medical staff and the governing board had relatively little knowledge of the hospital's earlier history; and even what Hutton himself knew of the heritage and early days was uneven, with peaks and valleys. They did not and may still not know (although they may care) what the physicians and lay founders had in mind; how policies originated and evolved or changed; the role that the medical staff and, indeed, the whole community played in the development of the hospital; or even which of the conflicting versions of certain important details of past history was correct. Some details had been revised through faulty memory and/or lack of handy records, but occasionally, it was suspected, for convenience.

St. Joseph's and Scottish Rite have a proud heritage and are fond of calling attention to it. Northside's truly grassroots genesis, and the altruism which drove it, are equally noble and distinguished. But only four years ago, after the Northside Foundation was recharged from its 1985 beginning, did the hospital begin exploring its past and reestablishing connections with some of its neglected early supporters. May this recounting nurture that process.

First on The Hill is really a two-part narrative. The first, which is the only one I intended to write, gives a long-term perspective and highlighted account of the years preceding the opening of the hospital (in July 1970) and continues through August 1973. This includes the era of the first administrator and ends before the other two hospitals were built.

Afterwards (which one might call "The Other Side of The Hill") sketches what has happened since at Northside and on the remainder of The Hill. This second part was added at the urging of those who felt a history spanning all of Northside's years would be substantially more enlightening and of greater general appeal, especially with the current intense national interest in health care reform.

This history should also shed light on a mystery: Why, in the most affluent part of the city, did this

"#1 hospital need of Atlanta," as it was called at the time, take eight years to build? It is hoped that a review of the obstacles and challenges encountered, and how they were solved (or failed to be solved), may help avoid some future difficulties.

The early part of the narrative is well documented. It is fortunate that I personally kept unusually complete records from the time of the first meeting in 1962 until after the Hospital Authority was formed in 1966. (In 1965 I was using these to prepare an article for the Sunday magazine section of the *Atlanta Constitution* titled, "How Not to Build a Hospital." This was a time when the Northside Hospital Association was at low ebb, and I never submitted the article.)

It was equally fortunate that my friend Hollis Cobb was a pack rat in retaining records of his civic activities, hoarding numerous newspaper clippings in addition to official records and correspondence. Hollis's records and mine overlapped until he moved to Nashville in late 1969. Together, they were ample. Since Hollis's death, his son, Alan, has kindly allowed me access to his records for this book.

The perspective of this account of Northside's journey and evolution since it opened has benefitted from a consciously solicited, broad spectrum of input — from governance and physicians to departmental managers, nurses and other hospital employees, as well as from some of the people who are Northside's sole reason for being, the patients. All four of its administrators have been graciously cooperative and reasonably candid.

Another reason for undertaking this project was that I was not aware of any in-depth, mildly personal history of any private, non-teaching hospital in this country ever having been written before, particularly not a grassroots one, and this would be an original contribution. The public generally has no interest in hospital history (and Harold Martin's *Atlanta and Environs 1940-1976* never even mentions Northside, St. Joseph's, Scottish Rite, Georgia Baptist or Piedmont hospitals). But I thought this one might be different.

As the narrative took shape, it became increasingly evident that many of the elements which appeared to make Northside exceptional were a reflection of the times. In a larger sense, the story of Northside is a case study of how an epoch of sweeping changes in this country affected a local medical microcosm, and the book is written in that context. In fact, the rise of The Hill mirrors the latter chapters of *The Social Transformation of American Medicine,* the 1982 Pulitzer prize-winning work of Harvard sociologist Paul Starr.

My final reason for wanting to write the story was that I thought it might be a fun challenge, the first of my formal retirement. I had previously been considered reasonably objective; now I was literally detached, and, as one of my former medical heroes, the late Ben Felson of the University of Cincinnati School of Medicine, put it, "Objectivity lies in the retina of the detached."

I have tried to approach this something like a painter or composer of music; i.e., as an exploration, without knowing ahead of time how it would come out. It has given me an opportunity to revisit and rethink part of the past from different perspectives, and to compare notes with old friends and a cast of characters, many of whom are still very much around. And to get it out of my system.

I have three regrets and one apology. I regret that I was not able to interview all of the many who were part of this history and would have been glad to add their recollections and their own perspectives. Perhaps this will encourage others to write their additions to this account. I regret that there are areas which may be too sketchily covered, and others that are too detailed, but this is a personal account, not an encyclopedia. I regret my inability to give credit to all the people, including unsung board members, who have played a role. I also apologize for the plethora of footnotes, but I felt these were appropriate for this kind of book, to provide additional information or commentary without impeding the flow of the narrative.

<hr />

Where I am now in all this is best described in the words of Sir Winston Churchill in 1949, when he received the Gold Award from the *Sunday Times* Book Exhibition: "Writing a book is an adventure. To begin with, it is a toy and an amusement. And then it becomes a mistress. And then it becomes a master. And then it becomes a tyrant. The last stage is that, just as you are about to be reconciled with your servitude, you kill the monster — and you are once again at peace."

1

Founding and Early Days

O n the rising terrain above the junction of two of Atlanta's major expressways — the I-285 beltway and the GA 400 gateway north to Dahlonega — is a unique cluster of three fine hospitals which is sometimes called "The Hill." More than 1,200 physicians now practice on this medical hill of Sandy Springs, simply referred to as the "Medical Center" in MARTA's plans for a station there en route to Perimeter Mall.

Of the three, Northside Hospital was the unconventional pioneer, with improbable and even inspiring beginnings from 1962 to 1970, when it opened. Soon after came two highly respected transplants — St. Joseph's from downtown and Scottish Rite from Decatur — to occupy two of the three other corners.

Like children, hospitals have an organic life of their own, not always growing up to be what the parents had in mind. We are what we become; we become what we are. This is the story of Northside Hospital and how it began. And what happened afterwards.

ᗐᗐᗐᗐ

In this country, the decade after World War II is traditionally remembered as a time of great promise and enthusiasm, oriented around family and home. But there was always foreboding. This narrative begins in the year when:

American troops had been fighting for two years in the Korean War.

Our government tested the first H-bomb, obliterating Eniwetok (Enewetak), an atoll in the Marshall Islands in the Pacific, in the largest explosion ever recorded by man.

After 40 years of service in the Army, Dwight Eisenhower defeated Adlai Stevenson in a landslide, ending 20 years of Democratic presidency, and becoming "serene grandfather" to the country. Television came into full play for the first time, giving millions of the electorate a first-row view of the candidates and the conventions. (Color TV would come a year later.)

Elizabeth became queen of England, Batista seized power in Cuba, "Don't Cry for Me" Eva Peron died in Argentina, and Albert Schweitzer won the Nobel Peace Prize.

Christine Jorgensen was the first transsexual to have a sex change made public, the UN drafted a convention on women's rights, and the U.N. Security Council held its first meeting in its new headquarters in New York.

A mechanical heart was used for the first time in a human patient (temporarily during an operation), the first artificial heart valve was implanted in humans, and electric shock was first used to treat cardiac arrest.

It was the year before the Salk polio vaccine was tested successfully in young children and adults, and the first human pregnancies were produced with frozen sperm.

Air conditioning for cars was developed, atomic bomb shelters for the home were touted, and Jacques Cousteau began undersea archaeology off the coast of Marseilles.

In Hollywood, High Noon, with Grace Kelly and Gary Cooper, was nominated for an Academy Award as "Best Picture of the Year," but The Greatest Show on Earth won.

Controversy raged in Georgia over the "county unit system," which gave disproportionate political clout to rural citizens in lightly populated counties.

Atlanta was four years past its centennial. William Hartsfield, Atlanta's perennial mayor, was still in office (he had been mayor in 1939 when Gone With the Wind premiered and he would last out the decade of the '50s).

The City of Atlanta passed its heralded "Plan of Improvement," tripling its corporate limits and adding 100,000 new citizens, to make the population 487,299. It provided for an expressway system, a new air terminal, an adequate water supply for the 21st century, a great regional public hospital (Grady) and government reorganization, eliminating duplicated services.

It was a year after cardiologist J. Willis Hurst (later Chairman of Medicine at Emory) transported an unconscious woman from Emory Hospital to the Peter Bent Brigham Hospital in Boston for renal dialysis, which was not yet available in Atlanta.

Desegregation in public schools was a decade away. Atlanta's first TV station (WSB-TV) was a year old, the Atlanta Arts Festival a year hence, and it was two years after Atlanta's street cars disappeared.

The year was 1952.

CHAPTER

1

▼▼▼▼▼▼▼▼▼▼▼▼

*"Cousin, Welcome to Buckhead!"**

In the summer of 1952, four physicians completed their residency training together at Grady Hospital and founded the first multispecialty group practice (apart from the Emory Clinic) in Atlanta, near the corner of Peachtree and Piedmont in Buckhead.

At that time there were no hospitals in the entire northern part of Atlanta, the nearest being Crawford Long downtown. Piedmont Hospital was still on Capitol Avenue in the southside of town. Grady, the charity hospital for the metropolitan area and the clinical teaching hub for Emory Medical School, was two complete separate-but-equal hospitals, one with all white patients, the other all black, connected by a tunnel beneath Butler street. Lenox Square was the Ottley home and grounds, and Phipps Plaza was still the Alexander estate. There were no physicians in Sandy Springs, aside from Leila Denmark, a pediatrician. (Forty years later, she was still practicing medicine in Alpharetta, further north.) There were two pediatricians in Buckhead, two general practitioners in Brookhaven, and three in Chamblee.

Since Atlanta's few major hospitals were in the central city, this is where the medical leaders practiced, and any young first-rate physician who did not aspire to practice at Emory or in one of downtown Atlanta's prestigious doctors' buildings was almost suspect.

The Buckhead Clinic, which was family practice oriented and lasted 19 years, was supersaturated with medical and financial idealism. Its four founders**

had been in medical school during World War II and had all served in a two to three year Army or Navy hiatus before returning to complete residency training. Its first financial advisor was Ralph A. Huie, Sr., father of one of the doctors. Huie, Sr., head of the downtown branch of the First National Bank and one-time treasurer of the city of Atlanta, was a devout believer that (a) practicing medicine was a noble privilege and a sacred trust, and that doctors should give their all for patient care and (b) doctors should not make any money. The group heeded his words and for some time they pursued both goals with equal vigor.

House calls were deemed one of the obligatory ingredients of good medical care, and, since there was no hospital emergency room nearby, it was often necessary to meet patients at night at the clinic, where minor surgical facilities, medical supplies, lab tests and X-rays were available.

When the growing clinic moved to new quarters, the entrance was on a side street, where no street lights were present, and it was necessary to focus a small floodlight on the name and street number of the clinic (which were recorded on a concrete slab facing Peachtree Road) so that patients could find their way. One physician was so offended by this, which he labeled as "advertising," that he sent a written, unsigned complaint to the Fulton County Medical Society. The Medical Society, taking even anonymous complaints seriously, determined that the clinic was not guilty of advertising, but reached a compromise whereby the clinic agreed to reduce

---

*Greeting by R.E. "Red" Dorough, real estate developer and self-styled "mayor of Buckhead."

**Ralph A. Huie, Jr. (internal medicine and cardiology), John McClure (surgery), Gerald Sutterfield (obstetrics-gynecology) and the author (diagnostic radiology and internal medicine). At that time general internists and general pediatricians were considered specialists; the majority of doctors were still general practitioners.

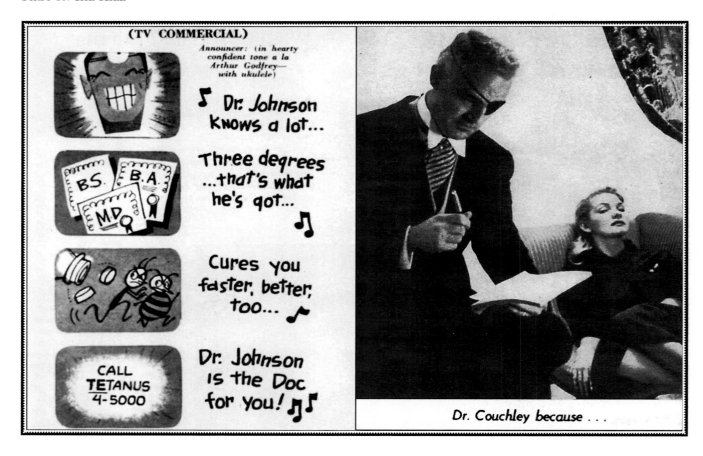

Dr. Couchley because . . .

the wattage of the light!

Although times were changing in Atlanta, there was still a strongly conservative sense of medical decorum and propriety. A journal called *Medical Economics* published a series of satirical cartoons under the heading "If Doctors Advertised." At that time the notion was so preposterous that the cartoons were considered hilarious.

In 1955, John McCoy (internal medicine), a North Carolinian fresh from the Army, was the first addition to the clinic. Other members who would also later play a role in Northside's history were Gordon Azar (internal medicine), Dan Kahle (OB-Gyn), Preston Miller (internal medicine), Keith Quarterman (surgery) and John Hall (internal medicine-gastroenterology).

The spearhead of Emory and Grady graduates which began in Buckhead in 1952, was followed by classmates Jerome Berman (pediatrics) in 1953, and Grattan C. "Chip" Woodson, Jr. (internal medicine) in 1954. Sharing space, a year later they moved to Maple Drive and opened a second office in beckoning Sandy Springs, where they were soon joined by Lea Richmond (surgery) and Herbert Shessel (OB-Gyn). Thus began the Sandy Springs Clinic, quartered ini-

tially in an apartment above Mrs. Loudermilk's "sort of general" store. At this time Roswell Road was two peaceful lanes. In 1956, now officially known as the Sandy Springs Clinic, it moved to Sandy Springs Place. After the addition of Norman Berry (internal medicine), Vernon Sanders (internal medicine), Jack Spanier (OB-Gyn), and Michael Levine (pediatrics), the full-fledged clinic moved to Roswell Road, and in 1960, around the corner to Vernon Woods Drive, where it remained for three decades. (In 1992, most of these and neighboring physicians moved to a new location, the Mt. Vernon Medical Center.)

Several of those same physicians still practicing in the area in 1993 recalled that there was a remarkable spirit of friendly camaraderie and cooperation, and an unusual lack of competitive feeling between members of both clinics (which also extended to other new physicians in the area). For example, when internist Huie at the Buckhead Clinic became ill, Woodson, of the Sandy Springs Clinic, was asked if he would cover his practice part-time. He gladly did this for six months until Huie returned. Shessel from Sandy Springs also cheerfully covered for Buckhead's Kahle when the latter had an acute illness. Over several years there developed a bond of mutual trust and respect and a network of easy rapport which was to be vital in meeting the coming major challenges.

Although the influx of competent physicians was somewhat comforting to the large and growing patient population, the increasing shortage of available hospital beds and lack of facilities for major emergencies were becoming a nightmare. Piedmont Hospital moved to its Peachtree Road location in 1957, but this was little help. Woodson recalled that often he was able to have only one patient each in Piedmont, Emory and Crawford Long, and that frequently there were no beds at all. More than once he had to refer his really sick patients to Henry Jennings, a colleague in Gainesville, when beds were available there but not in Atlanta.

In 1957 the Hospital Planning Division of the State Health Department, under R.C. Williams, strongly recommended that immediate steps be taken to construct a community hospital in the suburban area at each of the four points of the compass from the downtown hub of Atlanta.

To the east, DeKalb County was first to move, forming a Hospital Authority in 1957, which built the 200-bed DeKalb General.* (DeKalb would open in 1961). The governing bodies of East Point, College Park and Hapeville in 1956, formed a Tri-City Hospital Authority, which built the 150-bed South Fulton (which would open in 1963). In the west, the Order of the Holy Family Hospital of the Medical Mission Sisters sponsored the 128-bed Holy Family Hospital** on Fairburn Road (which would open in 1965). But in the north it was not quite that simple.

For one thing, the north area was geographically the most complex of the four. Basically comprising the northern part of Fulton County, it extended from increasingly urban and silk-stocking Buckhead past Sandy Springs to bucolic Roswell/Alpharetta. But it also embraced adjacent North DeKalb, a slice of another county. Each of the components keenly felt the need for a hospital in its own immediate vicinity (and Roswell, in 1957, tentatively formed an authority, just as North DeKalb had done earlier, but nothing came of it).

Secondly, official Fulton County had its hands full. The Fulton-DeKalb Authority and its tax dollars were completely committed through 1983, to the support of always busy, always needy Grady Hospital, oriented to charity and emergency patients. There was no demand from the north area for a county-backed hospital and Fulton County was not going to invite one. There were three interwoven factors why:

(1) Of the four quadrants in metropolitan Atlanta, the northside area was the most affluent and most independent. Atlanta had formally annexed 100,000 citizens in 1952, there was a flight to the suburbs (most evident in the northside), and those living outside the city limits were quite sensitive to the prospect that the city would one day try to do the same to them, with the threat of higher taxes, more control over zoning, schools, etc. Most were already adamantly opposed to political domination by the city on general principles, and the fact that the city was becoming increasingly black as suburban flight continued (and therefore political control would probably soon be black), did not help. They did not want to give the city or county any excuse for annexation.

(2) The vast majority of the political, business and social leaders of Atlanta lived in the part of northside, primarily in Buckhead and adjacent areas, which were closest to the downtown hospitals. Many of these families and their physicians had longstanding ties with hospitals like Piedmont, St. Joseph's and Emory and their medical needs were more likely to be met by the existing facilities than those who lived more peripherally or who were relative newcomers. If there was preferential treatment, they were more likely to receive it. Also, a "county" hospital (read "impersonal public facility") was perceived to be a step down from the private hospitals they were accustomed to or would like to see in their area.

(3) The few blacks living in the northside were in the lower end of the socioeconomic spectrum. They existed in segregated pockets, and the area did not want to encourage any more. This was still the deep South, and accepting a county-sponsored hospital would be "tantamount (a favorite word of some politicians) to accepting and encouraging

---

*Earlier, a North DeKalb Authority had been formed by North Atlanta, Chamblee and Doraville, but ceased to function when the DeKalb County Authority was created.
**In 1977 it changed hands and has since been known as Southwest Hospital.

integration," since anti-discrimination rules would be a likely requirement.

On top of this, Sandy Springs was not incorporated and could not legally form an authority. Wedged between the city limits of Atlanta and the municipality of Roswell, the area now known as Sandy Springs is still prevented from incorporating in its entirety because in 1963 the state general assembly passed House Bill #88, in which Section 2 states: "No local act granting a municipal charter shall be enacted wherein any part of the proposed corporate boundary of any ex-corporate boundary shall be less than three miles distant from the corporate boundary of any existing municipality."

Now, in 1993, Sandy Springs is said to be the largest unincorporated suburban area in the country, with many of its residents still fighting a long-standing battle to incorporate in order to gain control over planning, zoning, local politics, etc.

Four years passed, 1958 to 1962, but nothing happened.* Conversations among area physicians included two topics with increasing frequency, volume and fervor: the needs of their patients and the doctor's frustrations and limitations in taking care of them; and second, the faults and deficiencies (in operations and policies) in Atlanta's downtown hospitals which they felt needed correcting.

The litany ran the gamut. One story making the rounds was that of a complacent local administrator who, when asked why his hospital did not have an intensive care unit, is said to have replied, "We don't want to attract that kind of patient."

Some of the administrators tended to be dictatorial, but even in physician-dominated hospitals, arbitrary rules and preferential treatment of physicians and their patients abounded. There was usually a preferred list of admitting physicians, and the "young turks" had to wait for operating-room time until the space was relinquished by the more senior or prominent physicians at the time.

Neurologist Richard Franco recalls an incident in his extern days when he was unable to secure a hospital bed for the very ill patient of one of the newer cardiologists on the staff, even though there were empty beds at the time, because the hospital had set these V.I.P beds aside for the use of its most widely known surgeon in case he needed them.

When internist Norman Berry tried to admit a very sick patient with meningitis to the same hospital, he was told by the admitting office that no beds were available. He then called the administrator, and again was told there were no empty beds. Undaunted, he personally scoured the hospital and finally located one. Relieved, he called the administrator for approval to have his patient admitted. He was told, "That's OK this time, but if you pull that stunt again, you may not be on the staff any longer."

In early 1962 core doctors from the Buckhead and Sandy Springs clinics decided it was imperative to formally band together and take the initiative.

---

*Elsewhere, the new 1,100-bed Grady Hospital opened (1958). In 1959, Lake Lanier's Buford Dam was finished, and Atlanta reached a metropolitan population of 1,000,000. In 1960, it became the second fastest-growing metropolitan area in the United States, adding one new citizen every 18 minutes.

CHAPTER

2

^^^^^^^^^^^^^^

The Doctors Organize: 1962

The Northside Planning Association (NHPA) was born in the waiting room of the Buckhead Clinic in March of 1962, "for the purpose of planning, organizing, developing, building and staffing a non-profit community general hospital ..." Its membership was purposely limited to licensed physicians since it was to serve as the nucleus for the future medical staff. Seven men held the initial meeting.*

John McCoy, who was elected chairman for the first year, recorded: "It is our firm conviction that only a physician is in position to judge another physician's abilities and qualifications. A hospital staff must begin somewhere. Seven men, who knew each other well by virtue of their association, and who had no reservations about their mutual integrity and ability, established themselves as the initial committee on credentials and membership. They invited to the organizational meeting on March 18, 1962** only people who would be acceptable as members of the hospital staff."

The association's number grew rapidly, but almost immediately it was confronted by a major challenge. A private investment group, with developer George Weymouth as spokesman, announced its firm intention to build the Metropolitan Hospital of Atlanta, Inc. in the Buckhead area. A physician would not necessarily have to invest to practice in this hospital, but Weymouth's proposal required that physicians purchase most of the stock in the leasing corporation

(which would own the land and building). The operating corporation would form the medical staff, lease and operate the hospital.

Members of the Planning Association found this proposal unacceptable for two main reasons: (1) The doctor's status and privileges as an investor would have too much potential impact upon his status and privileges as a member of the medical staff. Metaphorically, it was the entrepreneurial version of the golden rule, i.e. "Whoever's got the gold makes the rules." (2) It seemed impossible to the majority of the members of the association to operate an excellent community hospital for profit (with a reasonable rate of return to the investor) without either having the cost to the patient unduly high or cutting corners on services, getting less than optimal equipment, or otherwise scrimping on patient care.

It did not help Weymouth's cause that the hospital was presented primarily as a business investment, and that no mention was made of what the precise needs of the area were and how the hospital would answer these. Ironically, had this proposal been structured and presented differently, there likely would be a major hospital in Buckhead now. As it turned out, the Metropolitan medical complex venture encountered almost uniform resistance and/or non-support and quietly died.

The encounter further united and spurred the physicians. The NHPA rapidly conducted basic investigations of the three priority issues: (1) the

---

*The names of the seven founders were not formally recorded. Mutual recollections placed McCoy, Richmond, Silverstein, Woodson, Shessel and Legh Scott at that meeting. The seventh may have been Berry, Kahle or McClure.

**Several physicians practicing at Northside 30 years later still recall that meeting. Others who were present besides the initiators included: Keith Quarterman, Preston Miller, Louis Riccardi, Gerald Sutterfield, Jerry Berman and Bob Arnall. Vernon Hendrix, who was completing a residency in obstetrics, remembers that Dan Kahle's wife Urte brought the refreshments: coffee and Krispy Kreme doughnuts.

appropriate characteristics of this hospital in relation to this community's medical care and health needs, (2) costs and methods of financing and (3) potential sites. The conclusions crystallized from these 1962 evaluations would determine the direction and the philosophy of Northside Hospital for the next decade. They presented these findings to business and community leaders in October 1962:

WHAT TYPE OF HOSPITAL IS NEEDED?

The philosophy is of prime importance — it should be designed to serve the changing needs of this particular community, in relation to an overall program of planning for medical care in the metropolitan area.

This hospital should be of the general medical and surgical type, providing service necessary to care for the vast majority of patients but not duplicating expensive equipment which is occasionally used for a very specialized purpose (such as a heart-lung machine or the artificial kidney), when this equipment is available in other hospitals in the Atlanta area.

It would include departments ordinarily present in any community hospital, such as obstetrics, care of the newborn, oral surgery, etc. (It seems the unanimous opinion of the pediatricians who are members of this association that a department of pediatrics should not be established at this time, as this would mean duplicating many of the specialized and expensive items and services which are available at the new Egleston Hospital, but that an area should be provided in which young patients could be cared for during surgical and less severe illnesses.)

Studies are being made to determine whether this hospital can provide facilities not now available in other Atlanta hospitals, such as private in-patient psychiatric facilities and rehabilitation facilities. An intensive care section should be provided, and a progressive patient care program is under study. In the minds of many of our neighbors, an efficient well-staffed emergency room is perhaps the greatest need.

From the beginning, the bedrock of the NHPA philosophy was its idealistic overriding concern for optimum patient care, not merely as a goal to be inspired by, but a commitment to bring into reality. It quickly recognized, however, that in the real world the satisfactory delivery of medical care was ultimately inseparable from the issue of control.*

Once the hospital was built, a governing board would be needed as well as an administrator. Three strong convictions were key elements in its philosophy of control:

(1) The governing board, medical staff and hospital administration should all be partners, with each having appropriate input into planning and decision-making, and by-laws should be set up so that no one of the three, particularly the administrator, should be able to exercise undue control over the others.

(2) The medical staff should be a democratic organization, so organized by bylaws, etc. that no physician or group of physicians would be allowed to dominate the medical staff or obtain special favors by virtue of his or her position. The medical staff would have members on the governing board. These members would be selected by the medical staff, but the terms of these members as well as all other governing board members would be limited to a certain number of years.

(3) If hospital beds were in short supply, hospital admission would be based on patient needs and not on the influence, prestige or special status of the patient's physician.

Each of these compelling convictions arose from or was deeply affected by reaction to perceived prevalent abuses at certain local hospitals.

What would the hospital cost? A ballpark figure of $5,000,000 was the initial estimate for a 200-bed hospital, as recommended by the Planning Division of the State Health Department. The consensus of sources was that this figure would cover the cost of land, building and equipment, although an additional $500,000 would be needed for a capital operating fund the first year. It was projected that the hospital would be self-supporting in two years or less. "We have the assurance of several hospital administrators and accountants that it is common practice for hospitals to operate within their income, i.e. pay their own operating cost, depreciation, and accumulate some funds from the income to buy new equipment as needed. In other words, a non-profit hospital devoted to the care of private patients should be self-sustaining," said a progress report by the NHPA in October 1962.

*Until the medical staff was formally recognized by the newly formed Hospital Authority six years later, when the authority's own by-laws were written, control was not a matter of immediate concern. And in the first years after the hospital opened, the medical staff, the administrator and the members of the governing board were indeed working partners, most of whom knew and trusted each other from long association. Years later control would become a chronic, recurrent issue.

In 1962, five million dollars was a lot of money. How to finance the hospital became as much a matter of philosophy as of money. The doctors were soon to ask business people and other community leaders and public-spirited citizens, friends and neighbors for their help, but they had to present them with a well-thought-out plan. They reviewed their alternatives once more:

A proprietary (commercial venture) hospital had already been ruled out. (It should be noted that this was four years before Medicare and the government's liberal policy of reimbursing hospitals for their costs had come into effect. This new policy would make the private financing of new hospitals much more attractive.)

Raising the money by public subscription alone or by forming a non-profit corporation issuing bonds with a fixed rate of interest were pie-in-the-sky impracticalities. Support by churches in the community was needed and would be welcomed, but sponsorship limited to a specific church was deemed unwise, since this would tend to narrow the base of active community support. Support by foundations was hoped for, but overall support by a single foundation appeared unlikely.

After they considered the options, there seemed only one way to go, but it sounded like a good one: obtain 40-50% of the amount needed to build the hospital through government assistance under the Hill-Burton program and the rest by public subscription.

Serious widespread construction of new hospitals in the United States had almost come to a standstill from the depression years, beginning in 1929, until the end of World War II and a push by President Harry Truman. In 1946 came the Hill-Burton program, which made federal grants or loans available in constructing and equipping hospitals and other health facilities for which needs were established. Although it was initiated by the Public Health Service (following the passage of the Hospital Survey and Construction Act sponsored by Senators Lister Hill of Alabama and Harold Burton of Ohio), and was federal in scope, it was administered on a state level. DeKalb General, Kennestone and South Fulton all had received financial assistance under this program before it ended in 1973.

To be eligible for Hill-Burton funds, the project must be sponsored either by a hospital authority — an autonomous corporation established by the governing body of one or more municipalities and/or counties — or by a non-profit corporation. A hospital authority would be eligible for federal funds of approximately 40% of the total cost, and an additional 26 2/3% of the cost would be available from the state, up to a maximum of $500,000. A non-profit corporation would also be eligible for the same amount of federal funds but would not be eligible for state funds. It would otherwise have all the powers, rights and privileges of a hospital authority (including freedom from taxes, right of eminent domain, employees not subject to unionization, etc.). The formation of a non-profit corporation would not exclude future conversion to a hospital authority, if the latter ever became feasible and still desirable in the future.

The chances of securing a Hill-Burton grant seemed excellent since the area north of the city limits of Atlanta stood high on the list of the Planning Division of the state health department, which would first have to approve any Hill-Burton applicant. Some of the doctors harbored the classic physician discomfort with governmental alliances, but there appeared to be no hidden catches.

In applying, it was also necessary to document that the hospital would be financially viable. The hospital would also have to agree to take care of a small fixed percentage of indigent patients free-of-charge. The law itself prohibited discrimination by any assisted hospital, but said its conditions were met if separate but equal facilities were available in an area. "Many hospitals in the South aided under the program refused to treat black people ... The Supreme Court did not rule these provisions of Hill-Burton unconstitutional until 1963."*

There were also requirements for the hospital site. These included that it be centrally located in the area to be served, easily accessible by arterial traffic routes (travel time being more important than distance), preferably 20 acres or more in size, not prohibitive in cost, and provide no significant obstacles to layout, construction and maintenance.

*The Social Transformation of American Medicine (1982) Paul Starr, p.350.

To be centrally located, the site must be near the Fulton and DeKalb county lines, since it was to serve the adjacent portions of both counties. To be centrally located it must also be north of the city limits of Atlanta (this was also an eligibility requirement for priority accessibility to Hill-Burton funds), near the I-285 circumferential highway. In 1962, a hospital located closer to Buckhead than the geographical center of the area to be served would have the strongest immediate appeal and support, but the population wave for the future lay in the direction of Sandy Springs and beyond, awaiting the impetus of the yet-to-be-built North Fulton Expressway (GA 400).

As this was to be a community hospital, the doctors felt that the community should be involved from the outset, with a parallel organization made up of leaders of the community besides physicians. The progress report by the NHPA to business and community leaders in October 1962 stated:

> The doctors felt that decisions regarding location, corporate structure, method of financing, etc. should not be made by the doctors alone, but only with the advice and help of the community at large, as represented by a group of its leaders and civic-minded citizens.
>
> It is our concept that this organization should include members who have prestige in their personal, business or civic affairs; who have the ability to organize; and who have the quality of leadership. We should also have some who are specifically valuable in fund-raising. Specific skills will be needed … so that they may act in an advisory capacity in matters pertaining to law, accounting, real estate, construction, finance, etc. Certainly, these people should be of sterling character and without personal or political axes to grind …
>
> The executive committee of the NHPA is fully aware that there are numerous people who reside or work in the north side of metropolitan Atlanta who meet the qualifications for such an organization, and it has been difficult to know where to begin. At this time we have in hand a list of individuals whom we have personally suggested or have been suggested by others …

These community leaders needed to set up such an organization to tie in closely with NHPA, the purely medical group. Since an authority seemed out of the question, a non-profit corporation needed to be established, without delay, to receive donations and bequests as soon as it was evident there was sufficient support for this movement.

The NHPA physician group, now over 40 in number, invited approximately 50 business and community leaders to a meeting October 23, 1962, at the Atlanta Federal Savings and Loan Bank in Buckhead. The meeting was chaired by Col. William Robertson, a tall, blue-eyed, authoritarian, ramrod straight persona whom Lea Richmond had recommended as one who could be counted on to keep things in order. A temporary Steering Committee of eleven laymen and fourteen physicians* was selected.

At its third meeting on January 8, 1963, with the help of the doctor group, it obtained a formal charter for a non-profit corporation, the Northside Hospital Association, Inc.

The Northside Hospital Planning Association (NHPA), the physicians' group which initiated the Northside project and which served as the nucleus for the medical staff, joined with business and community leaders to form the **Northside Hospital Association,** Inc. (NHA) — a non-profit corporation which would eventually build the hospital.

Kindly Maurice Womack, an electrical contractor, personally advanced sufficient funds to take care of the expenses of incorporation. In late January a larger meeting was held, including representatives of service clubs, churches and other organizations, totalling about 100.

By May 1963, a board of trustees, with Allen Post as chairman, was named by the temporary Steering Committee. The latter was dissolved, and the beginning phase was completed.

---

*Besides Robertson, lay members included: Charles Daley, Edward Hansell, P.D. Ellis, Louis Dettelbach Jr., Hollis Cobb, Mrs. Ralph (Ailene) Uhry (mother of Alfred Uhry, who would later write *Driving Miss Daisy*), William F. Carter, Maurice Womack, Joseph Cusick and Earl Smith. Physician members included: Drs. Harry Arnold, J. Norman Berry, Amey Chappell, Ross J. Cox, Herbert Girardeau, John M. McCoy, Donald Rairigh, Louis Riccardi, Lea Richmond, Legh Scott, Herbert Shessel (also one of the founders of the NHPA and first chairman of its obstetrical section, he reluctantly had to resign when one of his children became afflicted with acute leukemia), Charles M. Silverstein, Warner Wood and Grattan C. Woodson, Jr.

3

Completing the Team, Securing the Site

There were a fair number of people interested in serving on the board of a thriving name-brand hospital with a track record, but, starting from scratch, it would not be easy (and it would take time) to assemble a strong, stable board of trustees to accept the ongoing responsibility and potential headaches of building a hospital which might not come into existence for several years. Understandably, many successful business people perceived their commitment at this stage to be an injudicious use of their valuable time. Others had long-time allegiances with downtown hospitals such as Piedmont, St. Joseph's and Georgia Baptist. But many became advocates, at least.

The first board of the corporation which would eventually build the hospital consisted of ten laymen (Allen Post, Eugene E. Adams, William F. Carter, Hollis Cobb, Richard Howlett, William C. Wainwright, Charles S. Daley, Alfred Garber, Edgar J. Forio and Albert Love) and five physicians (Drs. John M. McCoy, Lea Richmond, Charles M. Silverstein, Legh R. Scott and Joseph A. Wilber).

The most distinguished member was attorney Allen Post, of the well-known firm of Hansell, Post, Brandon and Dorsey. Post, a thoughtful, generous man, was awfully busy but was willing to serve as temporary chairman of the board until Bill Wainwright, executive vice president of the Atlanta Federal Savings and Loan Association in Buckhead, agreed to take over the post.

Of the ten laymen, three became dedicated long-term supporters of the hospital:

There was Gene Adams, head of the Buckhead branch of the First National Bank. Kindly, patient and low-key, Adams became the first link in the close ties which have existed ever since between that bank (now known as the Wachovia Bank of Georgia) and Northside Hospital.

And tireless Hollis Cobb, a natural-born Southern politician, who would have been an editorial cartoonist's delight. A jovial and outgoing ex-Marine, he loved to make speeches and make things move. Active in other civic organizations and proud of his resemblance to Dean Rusk, he would later be the first chairman of the board at the time of the groundbreaking ceremony five years later, and would no doubt have run for public office except for his family's move to Nashville for business reasons (he was vice president of Frost-Arnett, a collection agency).

A political animal in the best sense, Cobb was almost indispensable in the development of the hospital because of his personal characteristics, not least of which was irrepressibility and a wide network of contacts. Hollis Cobb Drive, adjacent to the hospital, was named in his honor.*

And there was personable Bill Carter, an accountant and attorney with Courts & Company and chairman of the Finance Committee. Judicious and sensible, rock-solid dependable and easy to work with, he was a good one to have on your side.

---

*Hollis's interest in Northside began with his own embarrassing accident in a Fourth of July celebration. He had lit a Roman candle, was holding it the wrong way and, Lea Richmond recalled, "The damn thing went shooting up his sleeve and arm and he burned himself all down his arm." A neighbor of Richmond on Vernon Woods Drive, Hollis became close friends with the surgeon after coming to his clinic office for emergency treatment.

The General Motors BOP Assembly Division was one of the major employers in the area, with its plant at Doraville, and its manager, Dick Howlett gave the hospital project a great boost by his enthusiastic and steady support. This was continued by his successor, Ellis Hamilton, in 1967, and by their company. Noteworthy among the four shorter-term participants was urbane Ed Forio, a retiring senior vice president of Coca-Cola, who was willing to stay a year. He left to become chairman of the Fulton-DeKalb Hospital Authority. "The time I can be of real help to you is limited," he cautioned, "because once you retire, your influence fades fast." He gave some good basic advice, particularly in the search for and evaluation of potential new board members, and helped boost morale.

Four of the physicians on the original board of trustees (McCoy, Richmond, Silverstein and Scott) were among the seven who had started NHPA, the doctors' group, and McCoy, who had been chairman of the latter, became the long-term secretary of the board. The doctors knew each other well and had a close working relationship. Silverstein had even known Richmond since college days at Emory when he had edited the literary-humor magazine and Richmond had drawn some of the cartoons.

Although McCoy, Richmond and Silverstein were most involved during that period,* several other physicians were quite willing to help and did so in key ad hoc committee assignments. Norman Berry was liaison with Hill-Burton's W. E. Euzell, chief of the Medical Facilities Planning Section of Georgia's Department of Public Health, and Chip Woodson was in charge of defining what needs and services the hospital should try to fulfill and/or initiate. Legh Scott chaired the growing doctor group in 1963, Berry in 1964, and Woodson in 1966.

An informal but efficient liaison system naturally evolved. It was logical that one doctor (McCoy) came to more or less represent the Buckhead Clinic, which at one time had 13 associates, and that one (Richmond) more or less represent the Sandy Springs Clinic and others in that vicinity. Silverstein completed the coverage, since he was the only radiologist

Dr. Lea Richmond
"Still At It"

in the entire area,** receiving referrals from and in regular contact with most of the physicians in both Buckhead and Sandy Springs as well as Brookhaven and Chamblee.

Bill Wainwright served as the first real chairman of the board, from 1963 to the end of 1965, and made a valuable contribution during a difficult time. During his tenure: (1) the site was selected, (2) the project was approved by all the agencies which had to do with health and hospital planning, and a broad base of public support was generated, (3) the non-profit corporation began acquiring funds, (4) the board of trustees, which had developed vacancies, was refilled,*** (5) an architect-engineering firm was selected and preliminary plans drawn, (6) a use permit was obtained, not without a fight, and (7) primarily by financial pledges from physicians, the site was purchased.

Lea Richmond's interest in fishing helped pinpoint and secure the site. While chairman of the site

*The other two Board members, Scott (internal medicine) and Joseph Wilber (internal medicine-cardiology), both on Maple Drive, were also wholeheartedly involved, but Wilber soon left the area. Scott moved his practice to West Paces Ferry Hospital several years later.
**That is until Dick Elmer came to Sandy Springs. Silverstein had opened a private office on Maple Drive in Buckhead in 1956, at the request of other area physicians not in the Buckhead Clinic, in addition to the radiology services he continued to provide for the clinic.
***Miriam Kleinmeyer donated her services as secretary to the board of Northside Hospital Inc. She recorded minutes of the meetings, kept notes and kept track of pledges. She was usually accompanied by her husband, Jesse.

committee (which included Cobb, McCoy and Daley), he was on a fishing trip with friend Charles Bondurant when he happened to mention the need for twenty to thirty acres of land.

The three Bondurant families lived on twenty-four acres of land facing Johnson Ferry Road, immediately adjacent to and south of I-285 at the junction with the cloverleaf of the proposed North Fulton Expressway (a.k.a. GA 400). Bondurant perked up his ears and told Richmond that he and his family wanted to get away from the construction and the encroachment of the city on their beloved rural environment. By this time the site committee had inspected and evaluated 12 sites, but the Bondurants' immediately became the unanimous first choice, and an ideal one, at the bullseye center of the area to be served. And, by the nature of the hilly, wooded terrain, which McCoy had surveyed by horseback, the site would be "relatively easy to landscape and unobtrusive to the surrounding community." Hill-Burton approved.

An agreement was reached (pending zoning) with a purchase price of about $6,500 per acre, the going price of empty residential land in the neighborhood. (At the actual time of purchase, in 1964, the overall cost per acre was $7,350.) Between the Bondurant land and Peachtree Dunwoody Road was the ten-acre Minhinnett property, which would also become part of the site.

Since the site preference was predicated upon the completion of the GA 400 expressway and its eventual extension to Buckhead, the Board had concern about pinning down the official estimate of dates, but was reassured in 1964: "According to S. P. Allison, Urban Engineer for the State Highway Department of Georgia, the State Highway Department expects the North Fulton Expressway from Peachtree Road (Buckhead) to the Circumferential Road (I-285) to be started within four to five years ... The Federal Government has given approval to the project. The estimates have taken into account the possibility and even probability that some of the rights-of-way will be tied up in legal negotiations. The County is now systematically acquiring these." This estimate was a mite off the mark, actually a fifth of a century off. The completed road, a six-lane tollway, opened this year (1993) on August 1.

Quick recognition and endorsement of the efforts of the Association came from all the right places: the

Community Council of Metropolitan Atlanta, the Fulton County Medical Society, the Dean of the Emory University School of Medicine, the president of the Georgia Hospital Association, the communications media and several civic and service clubs. Help and guidance came from the State Health Department Division of Hospital Planning, the Metropolitan Planning Commission, the Atlanta-Fulton County Joint Planning Board, the DeKalb Planning Commission and the administrators of several Atlanta hospitals, notably Dan Barker of Crawford Long.

No solicitation of major funds was made during this period. Contributions by a few individuals and civic clubs in early 1963 took care of expenses for the next year. The first organization to contribute substantially ($3,000) was the Buckhead Rotary Club, under the presidency of James Smulian, a neighbor on Trimble Road. (He later became head of the association, which was to continue for a time after a Hospital Authority was eventually formed. His wife, Betty, who later became a widely acclaimed business woman for her successful lighting company, Trimble House, which she started, is currently treasurer of Northside's board of trustees.) Other initial contributors were the Sandy Springs Women's Club, the Sandy Springs Business Men's Association, the Civitan Club of Buckhead and the Women's Auxiliary of the Glenridge Forest Civic Association.

In January 1963, there were 57 physicians practicing full-time in the area and at least 34 part-time; in 1964 there were 125 dues-paying members of the NHPA. Purchasing the land was one of the next big hurdles, but no major benefactor was on the horizon, so the physicians pledged a total of about $125,000. The individual contributions came in a little at a time and there was never any large surplus of cash on hand, but these physician pledges and their fulfillment made purchase of the hospital site possible. To secure the property before the physician payments arrived, the board's treasurer, Gene Adams, arranged for an $84,000 loan from the First National Bank.

In November 1964, the board purchased thirty-five acres for $250,000 (after having been granted a use permit by Fulton County), and thereafter sold about nine acres to the county for the right-of-way for the GA 400 expressway. In addition to the pledges from the doctors' group, the land was paid for by resale of land to the county.

Completing an effective Board and holding it together was a daunting concurrent challenge.* To some of the physicians on the Board who ordinarily had little or no daily contact with the world of business and industry, it was also stimulating, an eyeopener.

My own assignment on the board was to be in charge of public relations and its ramifications. It was in this capacity that I sought an interview with Ralph McGill, the distinguished editor/publisher of the *Atlanta Constitution,* at that time considered one of the most important newspapers in the country. (In 1958 he had won a Pulitzer prize for editorial writing.)

McGill was a forthright, courageous man, usually outspoken even on controversial subjects. Not the least of these was "the double standard for democracy in the South and the need for change." He condemned bigotry "with the thunder of an old Testament prophet" but he understood "the Southern heritage, its proud tradition and its terrible legacy — and the reformation which was inevitable." When Harvard University gave him an honorary doctorate in 1961, his citation read: "In a troubled time his voice of reason champions a new South."** He had a variety of interests, even championed the introduction of kudzu as a way of controlling soil erosion in Georgia's red clay. Kudzu turned out to have its problems, illustrating his own aphorism, "The fleas come with the dog."

I scarcely knew McGill personally, although I had seen him and his X-rays several times, when he was referred to me by Joe Wilber, his personal physician.

Wilber said he believed McGill would be willing to talk with me about the hospital and McGill graciously accepted my call. We sat in his old house on Piedmont Road in Buckhead, over a couple of beers, and it was a fascinating afternoon. McGill came swiftly to the point:

"Atlanta gets new major things done because it has a network. Most cities, particularly major cities do, Atlanta more so. Some of these people are quite wealthy, some not so — but all have position or personal prestige. It's not what they own or nominally are in charge of, rather it is their personal reputation and connections, built up over a period of time, that make and sustain this network. These people know each other, trust each other, and know how far they can count on each other. Many of them even live close to each other. (McGill referred me to a fascinating book on the subject by sociologist Floyd Hunter, the man who coined the term "power structure": based on Atlanta, *Community Power Structure, A Study of Decision Makers,* was published by the University of North Carolina Press in 1953.)

"In the case of a project of the magnitude of this hospital, you absolutely need some people who are part of this network or have access to it. If you can get four or five of these people on your board, you will be successful. If not, you're going to have a hard time.

"Atlanta and this network may change, but this is the way it is now and in the near future."

I asked him, "Could you give me some of these names?" He asked that he not be quoted, but he gave me an offhand quick list of about twenty names. No one on our Board was on that list. I asked him about Allen Post. "I would put him on that list," he said.

McGill concluded: "Having said all that, Atlanta is a growing city and there are a lot of potential or actual movers and shakers out there that I don't know, so look carefully, especially in your own area, in addition to the traditional sources of leadership." He wished us well and wrote a supportive short editorial about the hospital which appeared in the paper a few days later.

A new short list of possible board members was assembled and everyone pitched in to help. Prominent on the list was W. A. (Dick) Pulver, head of the giant Lockheed of Georgia corporation. Lockheed had 24,000 employees (4,350 of whom lived in Sandy Springs and 800 in North DeKalb).

Gene Adams, Hollis Cobb, and I together went out to Lockheed one day to see Pulver. Gene, who represented the First National Bank in the area, was known to Pulver, so Gene made the appointment. Pulver was very busy, and we waited for a long time after his representative and PR man greeted us in his behalf. Finally we were ushered in to see Pulver, with the PR man still at his side. Pulver was cordial but immediately said, "I understand why you are here, but I must tell you right off that I am on 21 boards

---

*DeKalb realtor A. J. Embry and C. A. ("Dusty") Rhodes, District Manager of the Georgia Power Company, came aboard. Embry's stay was brief. To broaden the geographic base of physician involvement, F. James Funk, a highly respected orthopedic surgeon who practiced in an orthopedic group downtown agreed to replace Wilber for a short time, and later, Tully Blalock, an equally eminent downtown internist, also joined the board.

**The South and the Southerner,* Ralph McGill. Little, Brown and Company 1963.

now, and I don't have time to be on an another one." His PR man then took him aside and said something to him. Pulver resumed, "However, I don't want to be rude — you have taken the trouble to come out to see me, and the doctor here has had to take the day off — so I owe you the courtesy of listening to what you have to say." Hollis, full of pizzazz, gave a beautiful presentation. Gene emphasized the highlights and I filled in the medical perspective. When we finished, Pulver and the PR man went into a quick huddle (I idly wondered whether Pulver would dare go to the john without him).

What Pulver said then was remarkable. "I say to you once more that I don't have time for all this. But — you are right — we do need a hospital in this area and Lockheed has a responsibility not only to help look after the medical needs of its employees, but a communal responsibility, too. I tell you what I'll do, if this is acceptable to you: I won't come to any meetings (I really don't have time for that), but you can list me on your board, and when you have progressed far enough that you are ready to do your major fundraising campaign, call on me and we will do our part!"

We left exultant. To make a long story short, he became the first Lockheed member on the board and completely lived up to his promise.

Obtaining a special-use permit in a residential neighborhood provoked a public brouhaha and 10-month hassle. The surrounding neighbors all wanted the hospital, but they wanted it somewhere else. As soon as the association obtained an option on the property, about 800 nearby property owners signed a petition against the hospital and engaged "a Tuxedo Road northsider who is outstanding in legal circles," (according to the neighborhood newspaper), attorney Benjamin J. Camp, in November 1963.

The neighbors argued that "continuation of high-class residential development" was the best use for the property and that rezoning would bring commercial activity, in addition to traffic and noise. The board was empathetic but tried to point out that in the real world there was no way that the high-class residential development which had characterized the neighborhood would ever extend immediately around the junction of two intersecting major expressways. And that, paradoxically, the hospital would give the opportunity to create a medical buffer between the neighborhood and the expressway system. With the help of the county commissioners in charge of zoning permits, the medical buffer could serve to keep out the development of commercial activity other than medical office buildings.

The neighborhood was dubious and feelings ran high. Richmond's ex-wife called him, concerned over a bomb-threat rumor. The author's then-wife was vociferously opposed to the location. Even some physicians, including Dr. Tom Sellers, who practiced at Grady and was long-time chairman of Emory's Department of Community and Preventive Medicine, were among the petitioners. Many of the protestors were long-established homeowners who savored their privacy and their independence and were resentful of the intrusion of the expressways and fearful of further encroachment by "the city."

As the only member of the board who lived close to the hospital site — four houses away, on Peachtree Dunwoody — it was my assignment to represent the hospital at a neighborhood rally against the hospital held at one of the nearby schools. The meeting was something else. One prominent local politician said, "We don't want any integrated hospital in this neighborhood! I will fight against this integrated hospital with all my might and for as long as it takes — you'll never get me in there!" (A few years later attorney Camp would be a patient there on more than one admission). Another impassioned speaker gave this dire prediction: "If you allow this integrated hospital, you'll have all those preverts (sic) out in the grass!"

This disturbing attitude concerning the hospital had not been overtly encountered before by the board or by the physician group, even though this was the tail-end of the era when desegregation was still both a red flag and a spectre of unknown and unforeseeable consequences to many whites. There was never any subterfuge with this hospital; it did not intend to allow racial discrimination in its admission policy or patient care. Of course, some critics said, it was easy for the hospital and its board and physicians to have and stick to this position, since the number of blacks who lived in the area was approximately 0.5 %. The integration policy may have limited some contributions, but after the hospital was built, this attitude about an "integrated" hospital never surfaced again.

Between the time of the first and second zoning hearings, the son of one of the Johnson Ferry Road families had a skull fracture. The youngster was first seen by C. A. N. ("Scotty") Rankine, a general practitioner in Brookhaven, who sent him to my office in

Downgrading of costly property values is certain... more suitable location urged

800 North Fulton home owners fight spot zoning for hospital

Some 800 property owners with heavy investments east and southeast of Sandy Springs in North Fulton County have banded together and hired a well-known Atlanta attorney to exert every means the law allows in a fight against spot zoning that downgrades property values.

This key fight that may check spot zoning assaults on home property comes from residents who protest a threat to locate the proposed North Side Hospital on a large land area immediately south of the point where Peachtree-Dunwoody Road crosses the Circumferential Highway.

The protesting home owners are heavy numbers of long-established home owners along Glenridge Drive, Spring Mill Lane,

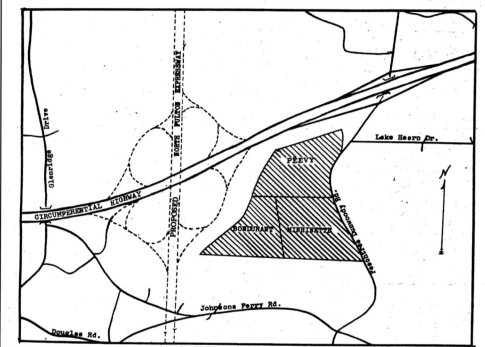

North Side Hospital has options on 20 acres in the shaded area

Lake Hearn Drive, Johnson Ferry Road, Shannon Mill Road, Peachtree-Dunwoody, Dunwoody Road, the Royervista area, High Point Road, Kingston Drive, Douglas Road, Hammond Drive, Sunset Forest Drive, Crestline Valley Drive, Pinebrook Drive, Timber Lane Terrace, Trimble Road.

The aroused property owners are not fighting the establishment of the proposed North Side hospital. They grant quite freely that the hospital is needed and they wholly endorse its establishment. They believe, though, that a more suitable location can be found for the badly-needed institution rather than in the heart of choice residential property along Peachtree-Dunwoody Road between the Circumferential Highway and Johnsons Ferry Road.

* * *

A PETITION which the 800 or more have signed stresses:

"This is encroachment of the worst sort in one of the finest residential sections of Fulton County. Rezoning of residential land for the hospital will necessarily bring auxiliary commercial activities which normally are established in the vicinity of such an institution.

From The North Side News, *November 21, 1963*

Buckhead for skull X-rays. Egleston, the children's hospital at Emory, had no empty beds, and it took some doing to get him admitted for observation at Piedmont before later transferral to Egleston.

The mother had been vehemently against the hospital location prior to the first zoning hearing. I happened to be attending a conference at Egleston when the mother stopped me in the hallway. "I just want to apologize to you," she said. "Not until it happened to me and my family did I really understand what all of you doctors have been saying."

On September 3, 1964, the County Commissioners granted the special-use permit, in a meeting reported in the local paper to be "enlivened by tears and jeers." In January 1965 , three neighbors tried an injunction against the hospital but it was turned down, and the matter was closed.

Since it was clear that the anxiety and/or antagonism of some of the neighbors was related to misinformation or lack of information, Gene Adams and I undertook the task of liaison. We met with several of them to allay their fears and responded to any and all questions about the hospital that we knew the answers to. There were three remaining concerns of the neighbors: (a) keeping as many trees as possible on the hospital property, (b) whether the board would actively support the neighborhood in keeping out commercial development and (c) whether members of the board would try quietly to buy property around the hospital for development for their own personal gain.

We received solemn promises from the builders and architects that special effort would be made to preserve the beautifully wooded nature of the property, and relayed these assurances to the neighbors. (To our subsequent dismay, the neighbors' fears were realized, and most of the trees came down. Jim and Betty Smulian still teasingly remind me about these promises not kept.) The board chickened out and decided it did not want to get involved one way or another in future zoning hearings in the area. It did not object to any of its members expressing or following their own personal convictions, as long as they made it clear that they were not representing the hospital. Individual members of the board, including myself, assured inquiring neighbors that they would not try to buy property around the hospital for development or their own personal gain, and, to my knowledge, none ever did.*

---

*A few years later, Richmond's son, Lea Richmond, III, would develop part of the medical office buildings in the area, on property owned by others. Richmond was proud of his son's endeavors, but he recalls they also caused him discomfort, since some people assumed it was he who was the developer and owner. Lea Richmond, III, has over the years become a highly successful medical office developer. The Richmond Group now owns half of the more than 1.1 million square feet of medical office space around the three hospitals on The Hill, in addition to its activity in North Fulton and Gwinnett.

4

Loose Ends: 1964 and 1965

Meanwhile, back at the board, the assumptions and approaches in building the hospital were reassessed. In 1964, the number of needed beds rose to 250 and the rule of thumb in estimating the cost of construction of a general hospital (including land, building and equipment) had become $20,000 (some estimates up to $23,000) per bed. (In 1992, a widely accepted approximate cost of new general hospitals was $200,000 per bed!)

The authority route was recanvassed, just in case, but the results were nil. In 1965 the board even had a bill, #516, introduced into the state legislature (and it passed!), permitting creation of an Authority sponsored by two or more counties, even though the hospital would not be located in the sponsoring county. That went nowhere.

That same year a new factor in medical care, Medicare, arrived on the scene (implemented October 1, 1966), soon adding to the demand for hospital beds. This was only one facet of Medicare; the ramifications of its provisions would take longer to fully absorb.

The Northside project had slowed down. Bill Wainwright was a conservative, no-nonsense banker, but he urged the board to hire on a part-time basis an enthusiast from DeKalb County named Walter Purcell. Purcell was a dabbler in PR and promotional work who was proud of his contacts; he had been administrative assistant to C. O. Emmerich, former head of the DeKalb County Commission.

Wainwright truly believed Purcell would give the hospital project the push it needed, but after a number of months it appeared to others on the board that Purcell had accomplished little more than writing them a monthly bulletin comprised mostly of items which they had contributed and were already aware of. Purcell had good intentions, but he became, in effect, simply a cheerleader for the board, particularly its chairman, and a sometimes gofer. No one blamed Wainwright, but members felt this was a $10,000-a-year indulgence the board, with its minimal funds, could not afford, and formally recommended Purcell's services be terminated. Wainwright was affronted and resigned shortly thereafter, in December 1965.

During Wainwright's tenure, outside pressures mounted toward bringing a hospital into reality on the now-purchased property as soon as possible. Entrepreneurs offered to finance it as a for-profit hospital. Indeed, while Northside was going through its long gestation period, hospital chains and other for-profit corporations began eyeing the north side of Atlanta.* Purcell proposed to the board that an available 35-bed round modular hospital in Montgomery, Alabama, be picked up and moved to the hospital site by Lockheed helicopter, as a start.

It was at this time that Joe Taylor came upon the scene. Formerly administrator at the 200-bed city-county hospital in LaGrange, Georgia, for eight years, he had been fired for recommending that the hospital services there be integrated. He had since worked for the Atlanta Community Council under Dr. R. C. Williams. Affable and relaxed, but quite knowledgeable, he increasingly became a good source of counsel

---

*In addition to its other attractions, 80% of the physicians in metropolitan Atlanta lived within 6 miles of the Northside hospital, and there were 722 registered nurses living in the service area, including 523 in active practice. (Community Council of Atlanta Survey of physicians, in 1965, and nurses, in 1966).

for Northside. At the request of Wainwright and Hollis Cobb, he agreed to look into Purcell's proposal, although it soon became clear to him that Purcell "was no expert in hospital matters." After a visit to the Alabama hospital, he advised against it. (The hospital was later moved to Woodstock, Georgia.)

Wainwright was a quite respectable chairman, but, ironically, it was his resignation which forced the somewhat dispirited board into searching for a new style of leadership. It settled on L. E. "Luke" Swensson,* who, almost magically, turned out to have the hoped-for entrepreneurial dynamism and drive (as well as the required corporate business savvy). Recently from Chicago, he was Atlanta Group Manager of Sears, Roebuck & Company, Retail, and jumped at the opportunity to make a significant civic contribution to his new home.

Swensson was full of ideas, large and small. Unabashedly, he advocated that, in designing a hospital, attention should be specifically paid to the "little features which keep the customers happy." For example, the relatively lavish, large new Sears store in the heart of Buckhead, at the corner of Peachtree and West Paces Ferry roads, was characterized by an extraordinary amount of free parking space for its customers, and Swensson had the Northside Hospital architects provide a similar large amount of free parking space adjacent the hospital. (This free parking lasted until overridden by economic reality two years after the hospital opened; the Sears store and its wondrous parking lot are also no longer there.)

Once Swensson took the helm, things began to happen.

---

*It was self-effacing Gene Adams who persuaded Swensson to come on the board, just as earlier he had quietly convinced Dick Howlett of General Motors BOP Assembly plant and had helped recruit Dick Pulver, head of Lockheed. Later, after the hospital opened, he coaxed his boss at First National Bank, Wilburn Askew, to join the Authority.

5

The Hospital Authority (1966) and Fund-raising (1967)

When Swensson became head of the board in December 1965, the Northside Hospital Association had four strong new lay members: M. William (Bill) Breman, president of the Breman Steel Company; Dan Chinlund, southern regional manager of Western Electric Company; Morton S. Hodgson, Jr., vice president, Coca-Cola Company; and Julian J. Barfield, vice president, First National Bank. In addition, the lay member nucleus of Gene Adams, Hollis Cobb, Bill Carter, Richard Howlett, and "Dusty" Rhodes were present, and the six physicians (McCoy, Richmond, Silverstein, Scott, Blalock and Funk) were unchanged.

By 1966, Northside Hospital was clearly the number one priority on the Hill-Burton list of needed new-hospital construction in Georgia, and the Hospital Authority route was reexplored. This time the grapevine word came that it was doable.

Dr. R. C. Williams of the Community Council urged that this be done without delay. With the approval of the board (although there were a few misgivings about the unknown implications of this alliance), on February 16, Williams and Joe Taylor appealed to the Fulton County Commissioners to work with the non-profit association in establishing the Hospital Authority of Fulton County in order to get the hospital underway. This proposed authority would be unrelated to the Fulton-DeKalb Authority,

"which was primarily responsible for indigent patient care" in these counties.

The steady liaison efforts of Hollis Cobb with County Commissioners James Aldredge, Archie Lindsey,* Harold McCart and county attorney Harold Sheats paid off. On April 29, 1966, the commissioners created the Hospital Authority of Fulton County. No bond issue support was implied, but the authority could sell revenue certificates, in addition to making the hospital eligible for $500,000 from state funds, as well as assuring the public of continuous operation.

This was a unique authority in several ways. Foremost, it was set up to assist an essentially private, non-profit hospital to get started and to back it up if it had problems. It was intended that the hospital be self-supporting once it was on its way. To conform to protocol, the commissioners formally appointed the members of the authority, which would be made up of only nine, instead of the sixteen members (ten laymen, six physicians) on the board of the association. (The association would continue, separate from the authority.)

The commissioners accepted the nine members proffered by the association. The seven laymen on the first board in 1966 were Cobb, chairman; Chinlund, vice chairman; Swensson, secretary (he remained head of the association), Carter, treasurer; and Breman, Barfield and Hamilton.** The physicians voluntarily narrowed themselves down to two,

---

*Lindsey was an opponent of the hospital at first and blocked the zoning effort until Harold McCart gained the chairmanship and literally slammed through the zoning. Allen Post's firm provided the petitioning attorney. Lindsey later got on the bandwagon and even became a member of the authority and, for a short time, its interim chairman.

**Ellis D. Hamilton succeeded Howlett as manager of the GM assembly plant in Doraville and assumed his position on the board of the authority and the association.

Richmond and Tully Blalock. Although Blalock did not practice in the area, he represented the valuable support of many respected physicians outside the area.

At that time the authority hired Northside's first employee, secretary Aileen Pohl. Aileen worked out of a small office in Buckhead where one of her first tasks was collecting pledges. She subsequently was the first administrator's secretary, and then worked for Dr. Barry Silverman in the Cardiology Department, retiring after 9 years.

The hospital's first attorney, in 1966, was William Bath, a younger member of Allen Post's firm, Hansell Post. His services were partially donated.

Having cast the die in the favor of an authority, the association, under Swensson's leadership, planned the fund-raising campaign in late 1966. In his 'kickoff' luncheon speech at the Capital City Club to potential major contributors on February 28, 1967, Hollis Cobb said:

"All this preliminary work enables me to report to you that out of a total cost of $6.6 million for this new hospital, we have in sight $5.1 million from federal, state and county funds and revenue certificates. We need to raise only $1.5 million with this campaign. But here is the most important aspect, one I cannot stress too emphatically — to qualify for Hill-Burton funds and state grants in the next fiscal year, we must have all our $1.5 million raised in bona fide, three year pledges by June 1st. Otherwise, we will not be able to get our application completed and in the hands of the proper officials in time to be considered in next year's Hill-Burton allotments, and some other area of Georgia — where the need may not be as great — will receive these funds simply because they're ready to build or expand."

Three major gifts totalling $275,000 officially launched the beginning of the fund drive, which was organized by Grizzard and Haas,* an Atlanta-based professional fund-raising organization. Swensson, the overall campaign chairman, presented a Sears' check for $100,000 to start the ball rolling, followed by Maurice Egan, executive director of Lockheed, with his company's check for $100,000, and then William Canning, the plant manager of the Chevrolet division of General Motors added a GM gift of $75,000. There were other

substantial 'intramural' or 'family' gifts, including $100,000 from Bill Breman (Breman Steel). Coca-Cola and the Trust Company of Georgia also contributed.

The campaign to meet "Atlanta's #1 Health Need" in a service area which had now grown to 183,000 from 110,000 in 1957, was meticulously crafted. As he had promised, Lockheed's W. E. Pulver headed the committee to solicit special gifts (of $10,000 to $100,000). After the required approval by the Atlanta Funds Repeal Review Board, March and April 1967 were reserved for the public solicitation drive. Chairman of this general committee was P. D. Ellis, who ran a Buckhead insurance agency and was chairman of the Fulton County Board of Health.

It kicked off fast and furious with a box luncheon for 525 workers. A total of 679 volunteers solicited 3,030 prospects, including individuals and businesses, in the service area. Dr. Tully Blalock chaired a Speakers' Bureau of 34 doctors and laymen who appeared before 55 community groups. Cobb stimulated the organization of a Ministers' Group, headed by Rev. Gerald Jacobson, to contact the 100 churches in the hospital service area; 47 ministers attended a luncheon at the Wieuca Road Baptist Church. Three hundred women had a White Elephant sale raising money for one of the hospital's projected offices; three Falcon football stars publicly volunteered their support; and a two-year-old girl was photographed offering her piggy bank.

By the June deadline the $1,500,000 goal was surpassed and the final tally on the fund-raising campaign was 2,104 gifts (of which 1,417 were signed three-year pledges) for a total of $2,077,000.

─── 〰 ───

Under Hollis Cobb's leadership, the authority obtained state and federal matching funds in December 1967, after four months of negotiation with the state of Georgia. As the application forms were being filled out, one official raised a question, "How many black physicians do you have on your staff?"

The reply, "None," was not surprising, since no black physicians practiced in the vicinity. None had applied to join the medical staff, and very few blacks lived in the area. That answer was not quite

*Be (Mrs. Leonard) Haas was an Atlanta legend, twice named Woman of the Year (in Business and in Civic Affairs). Cited as the prototype of the 'new American woman,' she was known for saying, "A woman can say and do things that a man can't — she can disagree and crack the whip and no one minds."

Hollis Cobb (left), first chairman of the Hospital Authority, and
Luke Swensson of Sears, head of the fund-raising campaign.

Falcon football stars help shoulder the campaign.

satisfactory. The official advised making an active attempt to recruit one or more black physicians for the medical staff to insure that the application would not be in jeopardy if the question of minority participation was raised. The situation was almost ludicrous.

Where to go for help? Asa Yancey, the very fine medical director at Grady Hospital, was black, so he was approached. Yancey's response, in Taylor's fuzzy recollections of that episode, went something like this: "Fellows, I'd really like to help you out, but I have all I can do right here. However, I will contact some of the doctors I know to see if they would be interested." The relayed response was that they didn't have any patients in the area, the distance was too far to travel, they couldn't afford the time to attend the obligatory staff and committee meetings, etc. Yancey offered his name and said perhaps one or more of the other black physicians would offer theirs in support of the application if that would be of any help. Joe Taylor contacted them.

Somehow the matter was resolved. A quarter of a century later there are black physicians on Northside's medical staff; no one knows how many, since no one counts.

By this time in 1967, Joe Taylor had become paid consultant to the authority. Less than a year later, in April 1968, he would be appointed administrator. The Hospital Association had transferred all its assets, including the land, to the authority. To keep the board of the association from feeling like a fifth wheel (it had many of the same members as the authority), it was arranged to have their meetings together.

In November 1967, the architectural firm of Abreu and Robeson was given the go-ahead signal to draw in earnest so that the final plans could be open for bids by the following May, and construction could begin before the July 1 deadline.

6

^^^^^^^^^^^^^^^

Coming Attractions

During the fund-raising campaign and in the planning year that followed, the concepts of the basic character and philosophy of the hospital and its operation remained the same as the doctors had described early on: It was to be to be an "innovative hospital with a patient-oriented philosophy, designed to serve the changing needs of this particular community." Who could argue with that?

Chip Woodson was appointed by the medical staff as liaison in the planning process, as well as a coordinator of the many physician recommendations. It was a fertile period, with fervor dampened only by constant awareness that the budget was bare.

Joe Taylor, board members, and the architects (through their representative, Matt Jorgensen) were all conspicuously willing to listen and receptive to innovative ideas and alternative approaches.

I was named early (January, 1967)* by the medical staff as Chairman of the Radiology Department in order to have final plans completed and approved by the July 1, 1968, construction date. Confronted by the usual restrictions — space and money — plus some fiendishly placed supporting walls, I sought and uniformly received gracious and copious help from radiologists, X-ray companies and others in different parts of the country who were specifically experienced and interested in radiology department design, with an eye for early expansion.

Although five was the minimum number of diagnostic rooms we could get by with, architects Matt Jorgensen and Tony Deas could come up with only four. "I'm sorry, that's all the space we're allotted, and we can't change the location of the department," Matt said. "I think I can squeeze in a fifth room, if I draw it myself," I offered. In those innocent days the architects were amused but not offended. They did not mind my trying, and I did wind up drawing the room-by-room layout of the entire radiology department, including the fifth room, with their approval.

Long-range planning for the medical needs of a large, changing population is hardly an exact science. Obstetrics, for example. When the architects were given the go ahead signal in 1967, the administration at first recommended that there be no OB department! They then decided it should be small, smaller than the earliest projections of the obstetricians. The reason: at that time birth rates were falling dramatically in Atlanta and throughout the country, and there was a widespread excess of OB beds. Why? "The Pill" had just been marketed. Now the proud OB service, with its more than 8,300 deliveries a year, first or second in the Southeast, is the best-known and busiest part of the hospital.

From the time of the fund-raising drive until the hospital opened its doors, special features of the new hospital were announced at intervals in numerous progress articles in the Atlanta and community newspapers.

There was one feature which needed no introduction; everyone had looked forward to its coming for a long time: Northside's commitment to an "efficient

---

*Official appointment by the authority did not come until early 1969, after the authority had formally approved the medical staff by-laws and formally created the medical staff. Although the department was designed for early expansion (a feature which was a source of pride), the expansion route was blocked by the second administrator's placing a new A. M. Admits area needed by the surgical section in that space, since this had a higher priority at the time.

Emergency Room open 24 hours a day," with upcoming easy access by the expressways; also, "staffed full-time by physicians who are specially trained and will limit their practice to emergency care" was greeted with great enthusiasm by the residents.

Some of the other announced features intrigued them even more. Of these, the four most innovative and memorable were:

(1) The first comprehensive mental health program and community health center in Georgia (and the first community health center attached to a private hospital in Atlanta).* This included a 25-bed short-term intensive care psychiatric wing of the hospital, the first in Atlanta. There would be provision for at least the same number in a "day hospital" and "night hospital" (partial hospitalization) since "it has become clear that at least half of all of the psychiatric inpatients can be more effectively helped if they are encouraged to retain some ties to their family, job or schooling."

Services would also include outpatient treatment, aftercare (post-hospital follow-up) and a program of community education and consultation to assist agencies (police department and school system) in identifying, managing and preventing emotional illness.

The architecture of the unit was planned around the above description. There was provision for individual, family and group therapies, as well as attention to the "community" needs of patients, such as a snack bar, laundry room and pay telephone. The unit would have a home-like atmosphere, would not be identified as a "psychiatric unit" and would have an open-door policy; i.e., if the patient wanted to leave, he or she could not be forced to stay.

(2) "In and Out" Hospital (now known as partial hospitalization) for outpatient surgery and diagnostic procedures, "one innovation brought to Atlanta and to the Southeast by the new Northside Hospital." Under this system, now standard, the patient is admitted, receives minor surgery, blood or diagnostic procedure (X-ray, laboratory exams, etc.) and is discharged, all in the same day. This reduces the cost to the patient and to the insurer and helps cut down on the need for

hospital beds. (In the late sixties, the experience at George Washington University Hospital was cited as a good example: only 2% of patients admitted to their "In and Out" hospital service had to spend the night.)

(3) The Obstetrical Department featured "family centered care," whereby babies could be in the rooms with their mothers and fathers could go into the labor rooms with their wives. This would be a very popular first in Atlanta.

(4) "A patient-oriented hospital." Although hospitals are fond of reciting (and believing) the mantra that they are patient-oriented, or that the patient and his (or her) physician are their first consideration, Northside's pre-opening brochure in 1970 pointed out, "In our study of hospitals and in the experience of our administrative staff, the principal complaint of patients is a lack of personal attention." In sync with the often-expressed similar philosophy of the medical staff, Northside's earnestly benevolent administration wanted to convince its future patients that it really cared. Once or twice it almost got carried away in its enthusiasm.

Note this gem from the brochure:

"This philosophy starts when you enter the door. There is no admitting office where you wait long hours for your room. You are escorted or taken to your room immediately and all details of admittance are handled in your room. The same is true of dismissals. They are handled by the same staff person in your room. Except in unusual cases the same employee will handle all the details of your admission and discharge." If this plan had been financially feasible, it surely would have been popular.

The brochure announced another convenience for patients, family and doctors: 800 parking spaces. This truly was a great convenience, since all of the parking spaces were on easily accessible ground level (there were no parking decks there) and parking was free (until two years after the hospital opened. Then, faced with security, traffic control and maintenance costs, it decided it could not afford this largess any longer).

---

*This significant advance bore the imprint of Hollis Cobb. George Dillard was chairman of the Psychiatric Department when these plans were formulated, Bob van de Wetering helped implement these, and Charles Edwards would become the first director of the center when the hospital opened. At that time, the federal government provided "seed money," but no permanent funding, for community health centers.

Other announced features:

(1) A 7-bed intensive care unit and, to relieve apprehension, a separate 4-bed coronary care unit. Like the rest of the hospital, "these will embody all of the latest features of modern hospital design," with only the best monitors and other equipment. These turned out to be just as advertised.

(2) A helicopter landing strip, called a "heliport" (approved by the Federal Aviation Administration in August 1969), "the first step toward a projected air ambulance service for metropolitan Atlanta." At that time a helicopter ambulance service was already in Savannah. Northside would become the first hospital in Atlanta to have a heliport, but a helicopter ambulance, which cost $200,000 at that time, was never obtained.

(3) A "cookless kitchen" concept, "used by six hospitals in the country — none in the Southeast," was touted by Joe Taylor and his administrative assistants in 1969 as the solution to delivering food both hot and flavorful to patients throughout the hospital.

Under this new system, the hospital would buy precooked food and store it in large freezers. The day before it was to be served, the preportioned food would be put in a refrigerator unit to allow some thawing. The food would then be placed in a cooler just above freezing. When serving time came, the food would be taken directly to the floor for heating in microwave ovens and served "piping hot." The "cookless kitchen" was also said to eliminate the need for a dishwasher, for everything would be disposable, and would require only half the number of employees used in a regular kitchen.

By the time the hospital opened, there was no mystique left about the microwave, and reference to Northside's "improved food service" had boiled down to the simple statement that "meals are heated in fast microwave ovens on each patient floor, insuring that hot meals can be served promptly to all patients." What became of the "cookless kitchen" is a story in another chapter.

On the Road to Groundbreaking

The twelve months between the fund-raising campaign and groundbreaking became one crisis, deadline or hurdle after another.

An additional twelve acres of land had to be bought, and in a hurry, because the U.S. Bureau of Public Roads decided that Fulton County had not acquired enough land for rights-of-way and upgrading of an interchange on the proposed North Fulton Expressway (from I-285 to the Peachtree connector), and it would be necessary to use some of the hospital property. The urgency was due to the county's need to acquire all the necessary rights-of-way before an August 31, 1967 deadline to protect $11 million in federal funds allocated to construct the Appalachian Freeway (a.k.a. the "Poverty Parkway" and now known as GA 400). This late development was an unhappy surprise.

Faced with sharply elevated prices to boot, because of the very proximity of the proposed freeway, the authority bought the Hartrampf (formerly Peeples) property on Johnson Ferry for $57,500 and the Corbett property for $58,500. This gave the hospital a total of 26.1 acres. The county said it would give the hospital 1.9 acres, making a new total of 28 acres. But then Matt Jorgensen, the architect, found that because of the changes made by the county, 32 acres would be required for construction.

The authority offered Dr. Byron Hoffman, an internist who did not live or practice in the area, $90,000 for 8 acres, after getting the opinion of a con-

sultant. He refused. After Hoffman would not accept higher offers either, the Fulton County Legal and Land departments condemned the property in a suit. The authority obtained the land, but at the dear cost of $145,000, the amount awarded by a special master. The cost of $18,125 per acre was about 2-1/2 times the cost per acre of the original hospital property three years previously.

In 1967, hospital construction costs had also risen to over $30,000 per bed, versus $20,000 three years earlier, and the authority realized it would now require a total of $7.5 million (including equipment and furnishing, but not initial operating capital). Anything less meant it would have to cut down on the number of beds.

Another problem had arisen in latter 1967: DeKalb Hospital was prepared and ready for a major expansion, and had applied for Hill-Burton funds in the same time period as Northside's construction; yet only a limited amount of money was available in Georgia each year. No one questioned that Northside was the number one priority in new hospital construction in Atlanta but both grant applications were considered of equal priority.

In September, Dr. John Venable, head of the State Public Health department, met with representatives of the Community Council of Atlanta, including Dr. Napier Burson,* liaison representative of the Fulton County Medical Society on the council, about how to resolve this.

---

*Gastroenterologist "Buck" Burson, a long-time luminary on the staff at St. Joseph's and until the end of 1992 its Medical Director, had long been an unsolicited supporter of the construction of Northside Hospital. In 1965 he told the Community Council that Northside should shoot for 350 beds instead of 250. He did what he could to keep other hospitals from preempting Hill-Burton funds while Northside was not yet able to meet the requirements. Dr. Lamar Peacock also worked hard to support the creation of a "special priority" in an attempt to get funding for Northside in 1967.

The conflict was resolved by allotting Northside $30,000 per bed (the same figure as Northside's own newly revised cost estimate), provided the hospital was under construction by June 30, 1968. In March 1968, Senator Herman Talmadge announced the Hill-Burton grants: $7.1 million for Northside's construction, $9.1 million for DeKalb's expansion and $1.2 million for a small hospital and nursing home in Hiawassee. The grant came at a critical time, since earlier in the year rumors had begun to circulate that this "medical palace of Sandy Springs," which had been in the works for six years, would never get off the ground because of a lack of financial support and, because the project had dragged on so long, new proprietary (for-profit) hospitals were being developed to fill up the slack.

On April 5, 1968, five months after the architects were instructed to "proceed with all deliberate speed in the development of plans and specifications," these were submitted and approved by the state and U.S. Public Health services. On May 3, advertisements began for bids. On June 11, Bill Breman, chairman of the Building Committee, announced the construction contract was awarded to the Batson-Cook Company of Atlanta and West Point, Georgia with the low bid of $5,119,700, $144,000 under the construction budget. (Including all the odds and ends, the total construction cost was $5,845,423.) Construction began 18 days later, beating by only one day the June 30 deadline that had been set by state and federal agencies. Northside had come gut-wrenchingly close to losing all federal and state participation funds.

The biggest jolt of this hectic 12-month period was a stark personal tragedy.

In addition to his heavy-duty job at Sears and his intense preoccupation with keeping the hospital push on fast track now that his fund-raising campaign was successfully completed, Luke Swensson had a wife at home seriously ill with breast cancer. For relaxation he would sometimes get away on the weekend to a country retreat on North Carolina's Lake Santeetlah, in the shadows of the peaks of Snowbird Mountain. One such day, with Mrs. Swensson reclining nearby, and having just laid some steaks to charcoal, he propped himself against the porch railing to wait until the steaks were ready to turn. Instantly, the railing of the elevated porch gave way, and he fell backward to the ground 30 feet below, landing on his upper back and compressing his spinal cord.

I went to see him at St. Joseph's Infirmary in downtown Atlanta, where he was transported. At that time he was paralyzed from the neck down. He was glad to see me and smiled. "How are the bids coming?" were his first words. (He had sent a telegram to the board, "I'M GOING TO MISS THIS LONG AWAITED HISTORIC OCCASION OF THE OPENING OF THE BIDS. HAVE FUN — BRING THEM IN LOW.") I told him. "That's great," he said, and smiled again. I've never forgotten his face. He was an extraordinary man. He died a few days later.

John McCoy was quickly pressed into service and he effectively took over Swensson's place as secretary of the authority. The "can do" esprit of Northside's leadership would never be quite the same again, but by now the seasoned members of the board had been through a lot together, and quickly regrouped to prepare for next month's groundbreaking.

Befitting the occasion, state, county and community leaders joined the hospital officials and the medical staff to celebrate.* Turning of the traditional spade of dirt on August 12, 1968, was more than a ceremony — it was the long-awaited watershed event and sea change. For the first time Northside Hospital was a reality. From this point onward until the hospital opened its doors, there was relatively smooth sailing, and all was right in this microcosm.

Construction was not without its share of incidents.

---

*Five people shared the honor of officially initiating the digging: Hollis Cobb, authority chairman; Fulton and DeKalb Commission Chairmen Charlie Brown and Brince Manning; Gene Adams, head of the association (replacing Swensson), and Joe Taylor, the administrator.

John McCoy, now secretary of the authority, reviewed the history of the Northside movement. (A photograph taken during his presentation, showing him wearing a hard hat, graced the cover of the Fulton County Medical Society Bulletin in October.) The principal speaker was Fulton County Commissioner James Aldredge (who was also president of the National Association of County Officials and Commissioners). Introduced by Harold Sheats, Fulton county attorney, he lauded this "unqualified success," and reviewed the obstacles which were overcome to achieve it. Community responses came from: Lucien Oliver, vice president of the southern territory, Sears, Roebuck Co.; Dr. John Venable, director of the State Public Health Department; Fletcher Thompson, 5th district congressman; and Dr. Judson L. Hawk, chairman of the medical staff during 1968.

Music was furnished by a group called, not surprisingly, "The Groundbreakers."

Dr. John McCoy at the groundbreaking, from the cover of the Fulton County Medical Society "Bulletin," October 1968.

A staunch environmentalist wrapped herself around a tree marked for removal and would not budge. The decision reached by Joe Taylor in consultation with the foreman beside the bulldozer was to wait until she got hungry. It worked.

The hot-tempered son of a well-known restaurateur, who lived on the corner where Scottish Rite is now located, had become so piqued when he learned the Northside site was selected across the street that he promptly sold his house. When property values adjacent the hospital rose rapidly, he realized he had sold too soon, and he became even more annoyed. While the hospital property was being cleared for construction, Joe Taylor bought one of the houses which was to be moved, and he used it both as a home and as an administrative headquarters during the period of construction. (He would later have it moved to another residential area in Atlanta.) One night when Taylor and his wife were out for the evening, the neighbor bashed in Taylor's front door with a car he had rented for the occasion. He was intoxicated at the time, his rented car got hung up on a stump, and the police arrested him. According to Taylor, the man cheerfully and politely paid his fine and the cost of repairs to the house, having derived considerable satisfaction from his dastardly deed. This may have been the same person who also shot a rifle through Taylor's living room window (again, when no one was home), peppering the living room wall with bullet holes. But this culprit was never tracked down. Years later the former neighbor was shot to death in an altercation.

The remainder of the construction period was blessedly uneventful.

NORTHSIDE HOSPITAL
FOR FULTON COUNTY HOSPITAL AUTHORITY
ABREU & ROBESON, ARCHITECTS
BATSON-COOK COMPANY, GEN. CONTRACTOR

Preparing the land, September 1968

WHAT NORTHSIDE DOCTORS SAY

THERE IS AN ALARMING NUMBER OF EMERGENCY CASES FOR WHICH DOCTORS REPORT NO HOSPITAL BED CAN BE FOUND IN PRESENT HOSPITALS. THESE ARE JUST TYPICAL

"A 42-year-old woman with rheumatic heart disease and a mitral stenosis murmur had cardiac arrhythmia, which did not respond to routine treatment. She was in emergency room from 9 A.M. to 2 P.M. before bed obtained. (I am sure the only reason they gave her a bed is because I refused to move the patient. Two other hospitals called and no beds were available.)"

"Unable to get bed for emergency patient at any hospital in Fulton or DeKalb County — even on a referral basis. Diagnosis — Pharyngeal abscess with difficult breathing — 103.6 ° fever."

"Ruptured Peptic Ulcer — 3 to 4 hours delay. Had to be transferred from Emergency Clinic in one hospital to another hospital because no bed in first one."

"56-year-old man with heart attack — no bed available in two hospitals — Finally had to turn over to another doctor who admitted patient to a hospital 12 miles from his home."

CONSTRUCTION HAS BEGUN ON THE NEW NORTHSIDE HOSPITAL

Located on the Perimeter Highway at the intersection of Peachtree Dunwoody Road, Johnson Ferry Road and the new North Fulton Expressway.

"Your LIFE May Depend On It."

WHEN MINUTES COUNT AND LIVES ARE AT STAKE

Northside Atlanta, the fastest growing and most affluent area of our city, with over 183,000 residents, is the ONLY section which has been completely without community hospital facilities. During the peak traffic periods a victim of an accident or an emergency patient in our section might as well be in some remote rural area for all the good present Atlanta hospitals can do him.

To quote Mr. William Pinkston, Superintendent of Grady Hospital: *"Unless we get helicopter ambulances, in a very few years it is going to be impossible to make emergency calls north of Buckhead during traffic rush periods."*

In a recent survey 73 doctors who practice on the Northside reported 84 emergency cases in JUST ONE MONTH where lack of hospital facilities or delay in reaching the hospital endangered the patient's life.

IF YOU LIVE ON THE NORTHSIDE, YOUR LIFE MAY DEPEND ON THE NEW NORTHSIDE HOSPITAL, NOW UNDER CONSTRUCTION

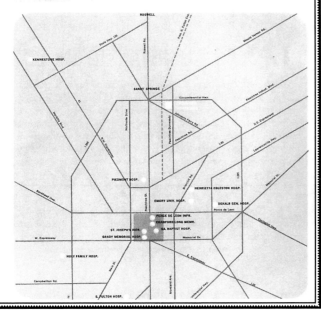

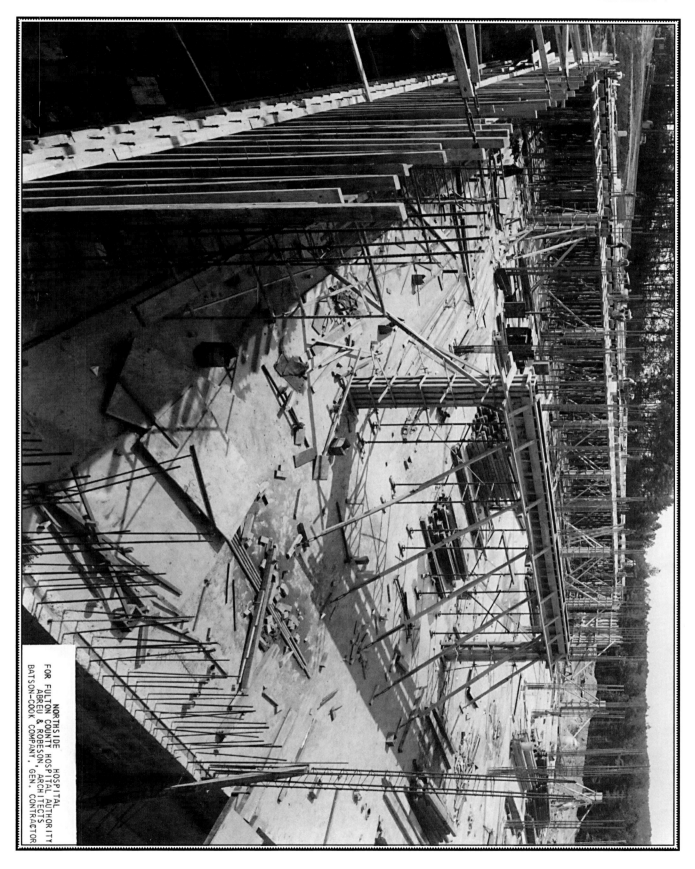

NORTHSIDE HOSPITAL
FOR FULTON COUNTY HOSPITAL AUTHORITY
ABREU & ROBESON, ARCHITECTS
BATSON—COOK COMPANY, GEN. CONTRACTOR

Construction underway, October 1968

NORTHSIDE HOSPITAL
FOR FULTON COUNTY HOSPITAL AUTHORITY
ABREU & ROBESON, ARCHITECTS
BATSON-COOK COMPANY, GEN. CONTRACTOR

The hospital begins to take shape.

A Singular Medical Staff

When Northside opened in 1970, there had probably never been a medical staff quite like this one.

First, there was the long (8-year) steady period of organized evolution. In 1962 it had self-started with seven men; before the hospital opened there would be over 203 members of the staff, over 93% specialists, approved by the authority, and at least 35 others still in the painstaking credentialing process. In those days all physicians who were certified by specialty boards (including internists and pediatricians) were considered specialists. In 1962, 43% of all physicians in the United States were general practitioners, according to Steven A. Schroeder, M.D., president of the Robert Wood Johnson Foundation. Dr. David Satcher, on a 1993 Clinton advisory panel, said 1962 was the year when health care professionals increasingly began to specialize, and increasingly obtained board certification.

The long gestation was, of course, not due to design but simply because it took so long to get the hospital built. The one benefit of that, at least prior to 1968, was that most members learned to know each other and each other's abilities fairly well. The downside was that, like an athlete who has worked out too long before competing, they were almost overtrained.

The NHPA, which had been planning and organizationally functioning as a medical staff since its inception, became the Medical Staff in 1966. However, it was not formally designated as such until 1968, when its existing by-laws were approved by the Authority. The membership numbered 121 in January 1966, according to Medical Staff records. By November 1968, the number of authority-approved members had increased to 154.

In January 1968, just after confirmation of Hill-Burton funds assured construction, the 90-man surgical staff asked the Authority for a moratorium on new applications for one year because these were coming in so fast that the staff was getting too big for the hospital to possibly accommodate. (There were six operating rooms plus two in the adjacent partial hospitalization area.)

The second unusual feature was that physicians alone had been the driving force initiating the grassroots hospital movement, and they remained actively involved in almost all phases of development before the hospital opened, including the pledging of the money which was necessary for early purchase of the site. Numerous dedicated doctors spent many months and even years of their valuable time without ever knowing, until the last two years, when and even whether their efforts would be fruitful. They worked closely and cooperatively together, and also with business people and civic leaders, muzzling their egos when necessary as part of the team, and for the most part exhibited enormous patience when progress was exceedingly slow. Their performance, in sum, was the complete antithesis of the stereotype of doctors-in-general (not one's own, of course) now in vogue.

Also gratifying were stirring efforts by physicians who, while not on the staff at Northside nor practicing in the area, gave their support to Northside's cause.* Tom Anderson, President of the Fulton County

---

*Mention has already been made of the contributions of Joseph Wilber, F. James Funk, Napier Burson, and Lamar Peacock. Frank Wilson, a surgeon at Piedmont, and Harrison Rogers, later president of the American Medical Association, were two others.

Medical Society (in 1992, President of the Medical Association of Georgia), pled Northside's case at the zoning hearings for use permit in 1964.

Third, this was a determinedly democratic medical staff. The heads of the medical group (and their medical specialties) from inception until hospital opening were:

1962 John McCoy, Internal Medicine
1963 Legh Scott, Internal Medicine
1964 J. Norman Berry, Internal Medicine
1965 Gerald Sutterfield, Obstetrics/Gynecology
1966 Grattan C. Woodson, Internal Medicine
1967 Cheney Sigman, Allergy/Pediatrics
1968 Judson Hawk, Pediatrics
1969 Keith Quarterman, Surgery
1970 C. Vernon Sanders, Internal Medicine

Three of these first nine came from the Buckhead Clinic, three from the Sandy Springs Clinic and three from elsewhere. The predominance of internists in this group (five of the nine) was a reflection of the fact that the internists played more of a major role in the early days than did any other specialty. This was no longer so after the hospital opened. As other specialties grew, the leadership was deliberately broadened. (In 1972 Robert van de Wetering would become the first psychiatrist to chair the medical staff, and oral surgeon Robert Bunnen would succeed internist Tully Blalock on the Authority.)

The core of the medical staff were the physicians already practicing in the area (and the Buckhead contingent would move almost en masse to Northside by opening time). Waiting in the wings were two other groups who were made welcome: numerous young physicians from recently completed residencies and fellowships around the country as well as from Georgia, plus physicians, well established or younger, who had been practicing in offices and hospitals in downtown Atlanta. Some of the latter, the group from Georgia Baptist was the largest, planned to establish second offices at or around Northside to hold onto their patients already residing in the area.

Both groups were intrigued with the prospect of "getting in on the ground floor" of a handsome new hospital with a highly idealistic philosophy of patient care and medical practice; a hospital in which, they were told, their input and participation would be solicited and welcomed by the administration as well as by their more established physician colleagues; a hospital which would show no favoritism to any physician or group regarding bed availability, O.R. (Operating Room) time or other hospital privileges; a hospital where the governing board, the administrator and the medical staff would be (and were already, from the beginning) partners. All this in the beautiful countryside of booming north Atlanta. These assurances were accepted like stone tablets. Medical nirvana.

The staff was wise enough to recognize that it had champagne goals but a beer pocketbook. It nevertheless believed that its continuing commitment, now buttressed by the support of many new doctors, could overcome whatever obstacles lay ahead. It was the once-in-a-lifetime opportunity to do it right, to practice medicine "the way it should be," and for a time they would be willing to give Northside the benefit of the doubt.

Understandably, the medical staff was not uniformly motivated or enraptured. Some specialty sections were not as cohesive or efficient as others. Consistent, up-to-the-minute communication and prompt feedback were not easy to obtain because the large, scattered staff was busy practicing at other hospitals and in a variety of near and distant office locations.

That there was initially almost no OB department was partially due to lack of consensus feedback from the obstetricians to the architects and to the administration. In the early architectural plans, a small delivery/nursery suite was located on the sixth floor of the patient tower. All other service areas — i.e., laboratories, surgery, radiology, etc. — had been planned on the ground floor for future expansion.

There are different versions of the reason for this lapse of participation by the obstetricians. The latter attributed it to poor communications, including by its section officers. Many of the pediatricians, who were obviously quite concerned, got the impression the obstetricians had lost interest and/or were too occupied elsewhere. Pediatrician Jud Hawk, who worked hard and long as first chairman of the officially recognized medical staff, decided to review the matter with Dan Kahle, chief of the OB section. Dan came thundering down to Joe Taylor's office, insisting Labor and Delivery had to be on the ground floor, where there was quick access to lab, radiology and anesthesia services. After weeks of discussions, the final plans moved an enlarged L&D suite to the ground floor and Nursery and Post-partum to the second.

EXHIBIT M

THE MEDICAL STAFF

THE NORTHSIDE HOSPITAL, INC.

Dr. Leroy C. Antrobus
Dr. Edward Leroy Askren,Jr.
Dr. William Green Avery
Dr. J. Hagan Baskin, Jr.
Dr. Loui G. Bayne
Dr. Fred M. Bell
Dr. Jerome D. Berman
Dr. J. Norman Berry
Dr. Stanley Perry Bickman
Dr. Tully T. Blalock
Dr. Richard E. Boger
Dr. Robert Louis Bunnen
Dr. Amey Chappell
Dr. A. Grigg Churchwell
Dr. Grady S. Clinkscales
Dr. Reese C. Coleman, Jr.
Dr. Leonard L. Cotts
Dr. Harry J. Crider, Jr.
Dr. William W. Daniel
Dr. Nicholas E. Davies
Dr. Charles L. Davis
Dr. Marvin L. Davis
Dr. Milton J. Deitch
Dr. Ray E. Dellinger
Dr. George P. Dillard
Dr. Joseph H. Dimon, III
Dr. Shia H. Elson
Dr. Jacob Epstein
Dr. Omer L. Eubanks
Dr. Louis H. Felder
Dr. William R. Fisher
Dr. Charles B. Fulghum
Dr. F. James Funk, Jr.
Dr. John J. Gerling
Dr. John T. Godwin
Dr. Joel I. Greenberg
Dr. James Cary Harper
Dr. Carl R. Hartrampf
Dr. E. W. Hathcock, Jr.
Dr. John Rhodes Haverty

Dr. Judson L. Hawk, Jr.
Dr. David L. Hearin
Dr. David E. Hein
Dr. Vernon J. Hendrix
Dr. H. D. Holliman,Jr.
Dr. E. Walter Hood
Dr. David S. Hubbard
Dr. William E. Huger, Jr.
Dr. W. Scott James
Dr. J. Trimble Johnson
Dr. Richard H. Johnson
Dr. Edwin Ladd Jones, Jr.
Dr. Dan B. Kahle
Dr. James A. Kaufmann
Dr. Hugh A. Klotz
Dr. Philip I. Krugman
Dr. James F. Langford
Dr. Michael K. Levine
Dr. E.P. Lochridge, Jr.
Dr. Edward C. Loughlin
Dr. P. T. Manchester, Jr.
Dr. Richard C. Margeson
Dr. John M. McCoy
Dr. C. Fred McCuiston
Dr. William L. McDougall, Jr.
Dr. Arthur A. McMurray
Dr. William A. Mendenhall
Dr. Harvey E. Merlin
Dr. Preston R. Miller
Dr. J. K. Mitchell, Jr.
Dr. William W. Moore, Jr.
Dr. William F. Norwood
Dr. Bernard H. Palay
Dr. William M. Pavlovsky
Dr. T. Elder Pearce
Dr. Edna S. Porth
Dr. James E. Pruett
Dr. Keith A. Quarterman
Dr. Donald W. Rairigh
Dr. Edgar O. Rand
Dr. Edward D. Reisman

Dr. Louis S. Riccardi
Dr. Lea Richmond
Dr. Ralph L. Robinson
Dr. Harrison L.Rogers,Jr.
Dr. Marvin Rothenberg
Dr. C. Vernon Sanders
Dr. William E. Schatten
Dr. Charles Scott, Jr.
Dr. Legh R. Scott, Jr.
Dr. Cheney C. Sigman, Jr.
Dr. Charles M. Silverstein
Dr. David T. Smiley
Dr. Douglas Smith
Dr. Richard B. Smith
Dr. William A. Smith, Jr.
Dr. Peter Chris Sotus
Dr. Jacob A. Spanier
Dr. Joseph A. St.Louis, Jr.
Dr. G. R. Sutterfield
Dr. Alexander Szecsey
Dr. Ben R. Thebaut
Dr. L. Newton Turk,III
Dr. R.J. Van de Wetering
Dr. Saul Vitner
Dr. Edward J. Waits
Dr. William T. Weaver
Dr. Seymour P. Weinberg
Dr. Robert E. Wells
Dr. Jay Herbert West
Dr. John D. Whitnack
Dr. Douglass G. Whitney
Dr. Walter B. Wildstein
Dr. S. Angier Wills
Dr. Grant Wilmer
Dr. Frank L. Wilson, Jr.
Dr. Thorne S. Winter,III
Dr. R. Warner Wood, Jr.
Dr. G. C. Woodson, Jr.
Dr. August S. Yochem, Jr.
Dr. Gerald T. Zwiren

**1965-1966 LIST
SUBMITTED IN JANUARY 1967
PROGRAM PROJECT NARRATIVE FOR APPLICATION
FOR HILL-BURTON FUNDS**

Board chairman Hollis Cobb told Hawk that he hoped the pediatricians' optimism about future growth was well founded because this late change had added $50,000 to construction costs. The pediatricians turned out to be right.

▂▂▂

From the beginning the pediatric section had been concerned not only about the needs of the northside area but with the larger issue of the adequacy of child care as a whole in Atlanta. The background is a tale in itself:

In the early '50s general pediatricians along with other "specialists" began moving from downtown to the bedroom communities of Decatur, Buckhead, West End, and elsewhere. Pediatric hospitalized practice was in special wings of general hospitals (Crawford Long, Georgia Baptist, Piedmont and St. Joseph's) as well as at the Henrietta Egleston Hospital for Children (then near Ponce de Leon Avenue) and the largely orthopedic Scottish Rite Hospital for Crippled Children (then in East Lake, Decatur).

Each facility had its own independent residency program, thereby having physicians in-house 24 hours a day for the sick child. These pediatric units in general hospitals had part-time directors, who also had their own private practice (and at that time the Department of Pediatrics at Emory was chaired by part-time professors as well).

Back then children always came first, according to Jud Hawk (now senior vice president and medical advisor to Scottish Rite Children's Hospital).* "It did not matter if there was no insurance or even if the parents could not pay when a sick child had to be hospitalized; the child was cared for as a "staff patient." Doctors in private practice volunteered their time for a month or two each year to help in the care of these children. The hospitals underwrote the cost as part of the teaching program for young doctors. In addition, for the indigent living in Fulton and DeKalb counties, there was always 'the Gradys.'"

In 1958 Atlanta's pediatricians were initially delighted when Egleston moved to the Emory campus in a new, larger (100-bed) facility, associated with the teaching program at Emory. Dr. Richard Blumberg became the first full-time professor of

pediatrics at Emory, and Dr. Joseph Patterson left his busy downtown private practice and part-time directorship at Crawford W. Long to become chief physician at Egleston.

Solutions often create problems. Pediatricians in private practice became concerned that Egleston's medical staff would be closed to them and, therefore, their patients with serious problems would have to be referred to doctors in the Emory Clinic in order to be admitted to Egleston. This did not happen, but many felt as though they had lost control of the care of their patients because, once admitted, the patient's care was "under the control" of the Egleston residents and supervising physician staff.

A year later, in 1959, they really had something to worry about. To up-grade the training of pediatricians throughout the country, the American Board of Pediatrics decreed that all future pediatric residencies must be associated with a medical school. This meant not only the end of the residency programs in the general hospitals of Atlanta but a significant drop in the number of pediatric beds available for truly sick children (so-called "quality beds") since there were no in-house residents immediately available to them. (The general hospitals still maintained nominal pediatric sections.)

In 1962, it had been the unanimous opinion of the pediatrician members of the NHPA that in the future Northside hospital "a department of pediatrics should not be established at this time, since this would mean duplicating many of the specialized and expensive items and services which are available at the new Egleston hospital, but that an area should be provided in which young patients could be cared for during surgical and less severe illnesses." By 1967, Egleston was too far away, traffic routes were too often congested, northside pediatricians were having to compete with the growing number of metropolitan area pediatricians for Egleston's beds, and they began to reevaluate.

In the northside area the children's doctors, mostly general pediatricians with a limited number of qualified pediatric sub-specialists, looked hopefully to Northside as a place to obtain "excellence in total comprehensive care" for their patients. In planning, their requests were mostly modest but specific: 10%

*In 1992 Hawk also became Senior Advisor for Children's Issues in former president Jimmy Carter's The Atlanta Project (a.k.a. TAP).

of the total bed capacity should be reserved for pediatric patients, up to age 15, in a separate wing appropriately designed for children (amounting to 24 to 25 beds). What they also wanted was an emergency room designed just for seeing pediatric patients, and, down the road, a residency program.

Their concern about the ability to take care of indigent patients was alleviated by Hill-Burton and Medicaid provisions, and this did not appear to present a problem.

Ralph Robinson, who was chairman of the pediatric section for several years, wrote in 1968 (in the medical staff newsletter, which Jud Hawk had initiated that year) about "the so-called typical wing": "This arrangement is far from ideal but is acceptable, as this area must remain flexible in order to provide for overflow from medicine and surgery." A separate emergency room for pediatrics was not acceptable to the hospital's planners. The 20 pediatricians in the section felt they would have to negotiate their future, but were willing to compromise for the time being.

The Northside planners tried to offer something for everyone, but the pediatricians, with reason, eventually felt they were once again at the lower end of the totem pole. Departments requiring big-ticket expenditures, like surgery, laboratory, or mushrooming radiology, were usually high on the priority list, but they were also a substantial source of income for the hospital. It was not easy to "think small"; General Pediatrics was (and still is) an unprofitable service for a general hospital. The pediatricians sensed themselves in the same category as nurses and schoolteachers, essential and indispensable, whose services were always gratefully acknowledged, but traditionally destined to receive whatever was left, which was not much.

The practice of pediatrics in the northside area and metropolitan Atlanta would change dramatically after the arrival of Scottish Rite* as a complete children's facility across the street after Northside opened. Jud Hawk and the pediatricians at Northside would play a key role in that arrival, but that is another story.

---

*The 165-bed Scottish Rite Children's Medical Center (SRCMC) now provides care through the more than 500 members on its medical/dental staff. Almost 100 of these pediatric specialists serve the clinic, which provides each month over 80 clinics representing 44 different sub-specialists and a multi-disciplinary team approach.

9

The Good-Guy Administrator

As the incoming administrator, Joe Taylor was the answer to the prayers of the members of the authority and, even more, to the medical staff. They liked all the qualities they saw; he was open, honest, forthright, friendly and empathetic, industrious, enthusiastic, curious, knowledgeable, reasonable, easy to work with and accessible. He felt (and twenty-five years later, still feels) that one of the major obligations of an administrator is to be accessible. He was decidedly informal, a characteristic appropriate for the '60s, and he was comfortable with himself and everyone else. If one had given him a quiz on all the right attitudes he would have scored in the top percentile.

A native of Wood Lake, Nebraska, Taylor graduated from the University of Texas with an electrical engineering degree and received his master's in Hospital Administration from Northwestern University in 1952. At the time he was appointed Northside's administrator, he was working toward his Ph.D. in business administration at Georgia State College. At that same time, he was serving as assistant director of hospital and health planning for the Northwest Georgia Health Council, Inc. He had joined the staff there in March 1968 after working with the Community Council of the Atlanta Area in a similar capacity since 1965. He had been administrator of hospitals in Mississippi, Tennessee and Texas before coming to the 200-bed City-County Hospital in LaGrange.

By the time Taylor was appointed Northside's administrator in April 1968, he had been so helpful to the cause that the nominating committee appointed by authority chairman Hollis Cobb did not even interview any other candidates. He had provided the

research data necessary to prove the need for this hospital and had prepared the feasibility report sent to Washington by the Atlanta Area Community Council which was a prerequisite before federal funding could be obtained. His program-project narratives in early 1967 included one for comprehensive community health service, and one for the goals, objectives and long-range plans of the authority itself, in addition to the overall Hospital Program. Conceptually, there was no aspect of Northside with which he was not thoroughly familiar.

Being a good administrator of a large hospital is not an easy job. In some ways it is like being president of the United States. Just as the President often epitomizes and speaks for the country to the rest of the world, the administrator officially represents and may symbolize the hospital to the public. When things go well, he takes the credit, and when they go poorly, he takes the blame. He has to answer primarily to the electorate (the authority) but he must interact carefully with and please other groups (patients, medical staff, insurers and corporate buyers of medical care, etc.) as well.

Nationally, the three branches of government (executive, legislative and judicial) check and balance each other. Similarly, in the view of the physicians and business people who planned Northside, as well as in Taylor's own mind, the authority, administrator and medical staff also would act as checks and balances on each other, so that no one branch would control or dominate.

And just as no one is completely qualified and equipped (by training, experience or personal characteristics) to be president of the United States, no one is completely capable of handling all the constant and changing problems and scenarios which are the administrator's lot. But, as in other complex chief executive positions, somebody's gotta do it.

The analogy goes only so far. The administrator is more directly responsible for planning and management, insuring a high quality of patient care, and for the "bottom line" (a favorite reference in the '80s and '90s), the financial status of the institution.

The power of the president, political scientist Richard Neustadt is said to have observed, is the power to persuade. The same is true of the administrator, who is continually having to convince the board and, in certain matters, the medical staff. One indispensable ingredient for effective persuasion is trust. Joe Taylor had complete trust in the medical staff and in the authority, and they responded in kind. He did not profess to know all the answers, but since he was honest, they could handle that and were willing to work together until the answers were found.

The only concern anyone had about Taylor before the hospital opened was that he had not actually run a hospital for almost five years. He encouraged and was quite receptive to new ideas. In fact, he seemed to be enthusiastic about *everything*. He was unusually trusting of the minimal administrative staff whom he hired and gave free rein. Well aware of his own academic leaning, Joe was a fine visionary and overall a good planner. But as a day-to-day nuts and bolts operations manager of a brand new hospital geared for the '70s, he was untried. He had worked well under Luke Swensson and Hollis Cobb, but Swensson had died and Cobb, the chairman of the authority, was transferred by his business company to Nashville in 1969, the year before the hospital opened. Now Taylor was on his own.

In retrospect, if he had had a good COO to run the daily operation, and a more experienced administrative staff from the beginning (plus some funds to work with), he could have turned out to be the ideal administrator that everyone had hoped for.

Taylor was completely in sync with the philosophy of the egalitarian medical staff, including its emphasis on a working partner relationship with the administrator and the authority, and agreed with its convictions about control and the importance of limiting tenure of members of the authority to no more than two consecutive 4-year terms. He believed a good balance could be obtained by having three physicians (all of them nominated by the medical staff

from its own ranks) on the nine-member authority, plus a fourth physician in a non-voting position, to serve as secretary. (In addition, the chairman of the medical staff would be invited to authority meetings.) Taylor thought this would insure adequate communication and continuous, fresh input by representative physicians in the most important phases of hospital and patient care matters, as well as assure their active participation in the decision-making affecting these. This, he felt, would also eliminate the need for a special committee (i.e., a Joint Conference Committee) to function as an interface in specific affairs jointly affecting the medical staff, administration and authority, directly or indirectly. As it turned out, for many years there would be only two voting physicians on the authority, and there would be a Joint Conference Committee.

These perspectives were reinforced by John McCoy after he was elected by the authority to serve as its secretary following Swensson's death. McCoy worked very closely with Taylor, who even today acknowledges the strong impression made on him at the time by McCoy's repeated enunciation of the medical staff's cherished views.

McCoy had done a lot of research on medical staff and hospital by-laws, and largely wrote the initial version of the medical staff by-laws, with Taylor's assistance. He and Taylor spent long hours at night discussing by-laws at the internist's kitchen table, and McCoy contributed to the writing of the authority's by-laws. (A committee from the Fulton County Medical Society reviewed the medical staff's by-laws [which were adopted in January, 1969], and declared them "excellent" and that "they should be a model for other new hospitals throughout the state.")

In Northside's history, McCoy aptly fit the description of the author's favorite definition of a "big shot": "A little shot who keeps shooting." He was not eloquent, not a politician nor a charismatic personality, but he was committed, thoughtful, thorough, forthright and tenacious. And it seemed he was everywhere.

The unhesitating support of the then-current (Vernon Sanders) and previous chairmen of the medical staff (especially Woodson, Berry and Hawk) was also a source of strength for the new administrator. He recalls that Jud Hawk "worked every Wednesday afternoon like a hospital employee."

Taylor also relied a great deal on surgeon Lea Richmond, the other physician most actively involved throughout the major part of Northside's history. Politically deft, Richmond also had a hand in most of the hospital developments. For a long time he was an effective leader within the medical staff,* especially at the executive committee level, with an ability to make insightful analyses and good choices in hard decisions, and had no reluctance to speak his mind. (After he became a member of the authority, he still attended meetings of the executive committee of the medical staff.)

*Richmond served on the authority three terms (the first two in succession), longer than any other physician, and has been the only physician chairman of the authority other than the immediate past chairman, Jack Spanier. He served with distinction, and in his time, became more influential (and in some quarters more dominant) than any other physician on the staff. Administrator Clark gave him special high praise for his ability to help arrive at a consensus or resolve some sticky problems quietly behind the scenes.

When a physician is elected to the authority, his primary responsibility is to the authority, rather than to the medical staff. In the latter years of the second administration there were more than a few on the medical staff who felt that Richmond, without his realizing it, had been subtly co-opted, his point of view and interests had not infrequently become closer attuned to those of the administrator than to the medical staff, and that failure to limit tenure had its consequences.

10

The Last Lap

During the many months of building, four already general impressions became obvious conclusions:

Many of the component parts of the hospital were inadequate in size, and early expansion of the hospital was an absolute necessity.

This was not due to poor planning. The architects, Taylor and the Authority all knew they did not have enough to work with and that parts of plans were marginal, but they were determined to build as much hospital as they had funds for.

To meet the construction budget, they had to arbitrarily limit the size and space allotted to each of the areas, and they became expert in stuffing square pegs into round holes. For example, Frank Wilson, chief of the surgery section, which designed and redesigned the emergency clinic several times, explained to one of the ER nurses that the reason the ER space, which was next to Radiology, was so small was that Radiology had taken some of theirs. But much of the shoehorned Radiology Department itself was cramped from the word go.

No one was pleased, but everyone was hopeful. The administrator and architects purposely used suboptimal, dry-wall construction in places, and used other expedient measures which would not show (such as providing virtually no storage space of any kind) to insure there would be no further delay.

Although in concept Northside was basically a "community" hospital, *its burgeoning medical staff — now growing faster, larger and more diverse than one could easily keep track of — would not long be satisfied with the hospital's self-proclaimed commitment to be simply of "the general medical and surgical type."*

The superspecialists were beginning to arrive. While this was a great plus for the patient and medical communities, these recently well-trained, medically sophisticated experts had their own special needs, their own special demands, and a high level of expectation of this open-staff hospital.

With its limited resources, Northside could not be all things to all people. Meeting the expectations of most of the 240-member medical staff (which would increase by another 100 during the hospital's first year of operation), was going to be difficult.

Because of their own steadfastly democratic philosophy, the "first generation" of medical staff leaders would soon be passing from the scene (unless they were on the authority) and new players, themselves destined for relatively rapid turnover, would shape the future role of the medical staff.

The lives of the physicians in the Planning Association, like those of Taylor and members of the Authority, had all been directly changed by global World War II, and their parents' well being and outlook had been profoundly influenced by the Great Depression. Too, these doctors' professional lives had all been spent in an era when hospitals did not have to compete, and board-certified specialists were far fewer. How could hospital and medical staff leaders of the next two decades have this same idealism and set of values, and the same dedication?

The 1967 fund-raising drive had successfully met Hill-Burton requirements for building and construction, but *Northside was still short of money.*

By the latter half of 1968, total funds received or receivable were over 12 million dollars (two million from the campaign, three million from revenue certificates and 7.1 million from Hill-Burton, including state-matching), but the total cost (including additional cost of land, operating expenses and provisions for initial operating capital) had risen to almost meet income by the time the hospital opened. The total cost listed in the newspapers was $8.5 million.

The sum of $585,000 allocated to the purchase of medical equipment was declared "pitifully unrealistic" by the equipment committee (Dan Chinlund of the authority, with Jud Hawk, as the Medical Staff representative, and Joe Taylor), which checked out each request of the medical staff repeatedly, and the authority authorized a new figure of $900,000. The final figure would be $1,100,837. The cost of advanced technology was jolting; in 1969-1970 three diagnostic rooms in Radiology cost $224,000. (In 1952 an X-ray room, including fluoroscopy, was equipped for $14,000.) Two additional smaller fund-raising campaigns were held, one for equipment.* The older physicians were getting weary of being called upon.

Finances were improved in September 1968, when Dr. John Venable of the State Health Department announced that $459,633 in U.S. Public Health funds were allocated to Northside for the Community Mental Health Center (which would have 25 of Northside's 250 beds), matching the $475,624 amount Northside earmarked in its first campaign.

The other remaining problem was start-up operating capital needed for the first year. In 1963-64, the estimated amount needed was $500,000; by 1970 this had doubled. The authority was keenly aware of this looming hazard, but all of Northside's limited funds were already consigned elsewhere, and the authority was not inclined to borrow. When Joe Taylor pressed for the needed million dollars, the finance committee's Maury Egan said, "You'll play hell getting it." Bill Carter was gentler: "Can you open the hospital without it?" Taylor responded, "Yes, but I don't recommend it." Subsequently, he wished he had just said, "No!"

The result was that Taylor had to open the hospital and make numerous financial commitments with no (i.e., nada, zero, zilch) working capital. Despite all the preceding effort, Northside's financial status at the opening was precarious and the impact upon the first six months of operation would be almost disastrous.

---

*Oral surgeon Bob Bunnen, chairman of the medical staff's finance committee, reported with glee that he had received an unusual check. The addressee was sent a statement by mistake — he was not a member of the Medical Staff nor even a doctor — but the man paid it anyway.

11

The "In-House" Physicians

To render good patient care and to meet the particular needs of surgeons and other medical practitioners, it is necessary for hospitals to provide certain specialized medical services, requiring the participation of specific kinds of medical specialists. As the need and demand for the services of these physicians have grown, their collective presence has been increasingly required full-time at private (as well as public) general hospitals and they have become essentially "hospital-based" or "in-house." Their services are routinely performed during the working day but they must be available for emergencies at night. As general hospitals have grown and become more sophisticated, these physicians have grown into larger groups and the range of their services and the basic services expected to be provided by the hospital (whether or not these services are available outside the hospital) have grown and expanded. Northside opened in 1970 with only a handful of such physicians; now over 65 of the physicians on Northside's staff are "in-house."

Traditionally, prior to the '70s, Pathology, Radiology and Anesthesiology had been the core of hospital-based services, particularly in hospitals without a residency training program, and this was true at Northside.

Anesthesiology: In the past, Anesthesiology had often been a sub-section of the Surgery Department in hospitals in this country, but, reflecting the newer trend, the medical staff declared in January 1968 that Anesthesiology should be in a separate department.

The authority agreed.

John Patton, from Emory, was selected head of Anesthesiology* in April, 1969. His coming was especially greeted with enthusiasm by the obstetricians, because of his facility and enthusiastic interest in epidural anesthesia. When Northside opened, it was the only hospital in Atlanta (outside of Grady, which was not a private hospital) where this type of anesthesia was readily available, and this contributed to the immediate smashing popularity of the innovative, user-friendly OB services.

John Neeld, from Emory, who joined Patton in 1973, is now chairman of Anesthesiology. The department now has 24 anesthesiologists, 31 CRNA's (Certified Registered Nurse Anesthetists) and 13 PA's (Professional Assistants).

Pathology: Ray Graves, also from Emory, was selected late, less than five months before opening day, as chairman of Pathology, and his small department was almost completed when he arrived. Rufus Kervin was working for the Air Force as a civilian chemist at Maxwell Air Force Base, Alabama, when Graves, at that time an Air Force officer and Director of the Laboratory, invited him to come to Northside to help operate and manage the clinical lab. Both Graves and Kervin have been at Northside since it opened. Chris Allan, Graves' first associate, in 1973, trained at the Mayo Clinic, is now chairman. The department now has 7 full-time pathologists plus 1 part-time, 120 employees and two PA's (Professional Assistants). Graves and Allan are among the more than 100 physi-

---

*Patton wrote of the scope of Anesthesiology at that time: "The anesthesia department in modern medicine should concern itself with more than surgical anesthesia (including state of the art monitoring equipment). It also embraces respiratory care, pulmonary function studies and blood gas analyses, and would function as a consultant to ER and Intensive Care and provide service to all cardiac arrest calls in the hospital … Every patient scheduled for surgery will be seen and evaluated by the anesthesiologist."

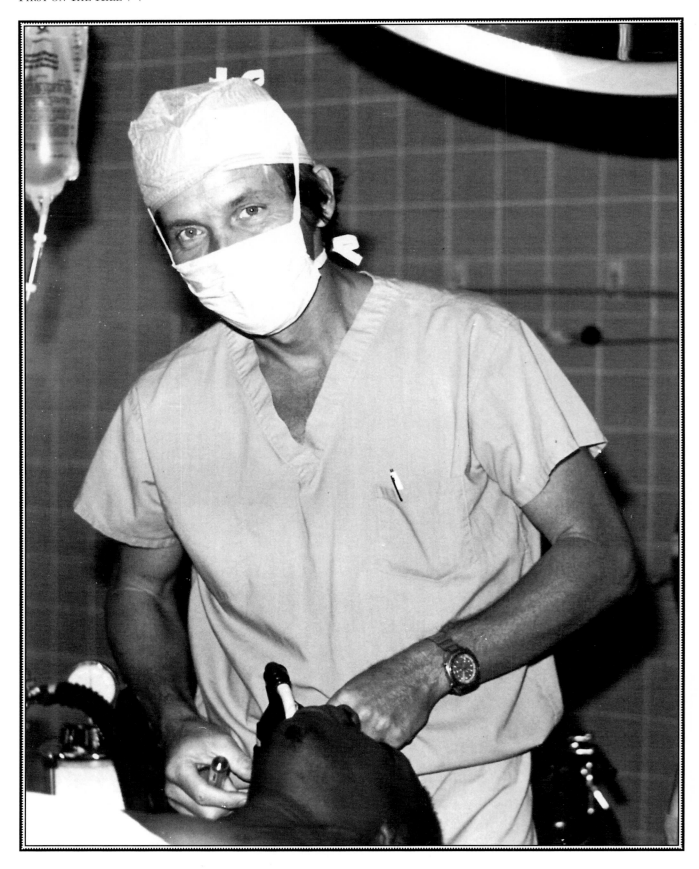

Dr. John Patton, first head of Anesthesiology

cians who have practiced at Northside 20 years or longer, and Kervin is among the more than 100 employees who have been at Northside 20 years or longer.

Three of the pathologists seasoned in Northside's service orientation later became heads of pathology departments at other Atlanta hospitals: David Stacey at St. Joseph's; Jim Bootle at Shallowford; and Charles Garrison at West Paces Ferry.

Radiology: Six months before opening, Neal Chandler came aboard from Egleston as the author's first associate in Radiology.* The second was Marshall Catanzaro, a St. Louis friend of plastic surgeon Harvey Weiss, in the fall of 1970, after he completed Army duty. "Cat" is now senior member of the group of 14 radiologists. We had one special procedure room (for vascular studies, etc.), and we provided for nuclear medicine (radioisotope scans of the thyroid, gallbladder, bones, etc.). Ultrasound was beginning to appear in hospitals, but only in crude, static images. CT and MRI were a long way away. We decided to defer radiation therapy; we felt it should be in a separate department, when the hospital could afford it. I had some experience in mammography (Emory's Dr. Robert Egan was a pioneer in this country and I was fortunate to learn from him), but the equipment and film were not yet good enough for our dollars.

〰〰〰

Emergency: While teaching hospitals relied heavily on residents and interns to man their emergency rooms, in the 1960s non-teaching hospitals began staffing their ER sections with doctors who devoted all their time to this type of practice and, later, specifically trained for it. DeKalb Hospital was a good local prototype. In March 1969, the medical staff voted to have full-time ER physicians, and surgeon

Ben Thebaut, in charge of the ER planning committee, interview prospects. Demand for such qualified specialists was high, but they were still scarce,** and the ER did not open with a designated ER physician in charge. Two of the first three ER doctors were temporary physicians from the Naval Air Station.

The other hospital-based physicians: Three years after Northside opened, Barry Silverman became the in-house cardiologist; three years later, Jim Wellman the in-house pulmonologist; and in 1977, after the first hospital expansion, Dale McCord was named head of the new Department of Radiation Therapy. Pediatrician Saul Adler came as the neonatologist the same year, and in 1990 radiologist Larry Stone and obstetrician Jeff Korotkin became the perinatologists.

〰〰〰

A pause in the narrative to take a brief look at the hospital-based physicians is warranted because (1) their relation with the hospital and its administrator is a little different than that of the remainder of the medical staff; (2) of the few differences, the most important historically has been the fact that they have a contract with the hospital (which is both a hospital requirement and a sensible business procedure); (3) contract differences were a source of major controversy*** during the era of the second administrator, and, to a lesser extent, of the third. Turmoil surrounding these recurrent controversies was one of the factors which lost the confidence of the medical staff in these two administrators and thereby contributed to shortening their tenure.

(4) Some of the medical staff had a degree of resentment and envy concerning "hospital-based" physicians because of the monopoly characteristics of their hospital practice,**** plus the fact that the

---

*The intent was to allow me three months leave, at my own expense, to inspect other radiology departments in the country and obtain further post-graduate training, but so many matters came up during construction, I was not able to stray far from the building site. The only solace was that Radiology was almost the only department in the hospital which was fully operational when the hospital opened. Chandler subsequently became chairman of the Radiology Department at Scottish Rite. In the early years of Scottish Rite, Northside's radiologists assisted him in providing services there.

**The American Board of Emergency Medicine, starting as a conjoint board, in 1979 began certifying physicians as qualified in this field. In 1989 Emergency Medicine became a completely separate medical specialty, the 23rd such.

***The problems came from two directions: attempts by the second administrator to impose new contracts containing provisions unacceptable to the in-house physicians, and — in their view — failure of the administrator (and ultimately the hospital, which he represented) to honor or carry out provisions of the existing contract. Most board and medical staff members were unaware of the precise contract provisions and the precise reasons for a specific controversy, at least, until it reached an advanced stage.

****Radiology pointedly resisted an exclusive contract, and voluntarily shared a limited segment of turf with the vascular and neurosurgeons, "in-house" cardiologist, laboratory etc. Nevertheless, for the sake of practicality, efficiency and cohesiveness it otherwise became, in fact, a virtual monopoly. The neonatologists, who also service Scottish Rite, do not have an exclusive contract either; in that situation, the Kaiser pediatricians ordinarily take care of newborns at Northside who are delivered by Kaiser obstetricians. As one would expect, each "in-house" group has evolved differently.

almost revolutionary advances in technology and equipment that were needed in radiology, laboratory, etc. were big ticket items in the competitive budgeting process which often crowded out requests from other departments and specialists.

Any tinge of resentment was reinforced when reimbursement policies in the latter '80s (continuing until the early '90s) rewarded procedures — surgical and medical, diagnostic and therapeutic — very well. Consequently, the incomes of procedure-oriented specialists, such as anesthesiologists and radiologists, joined that of surgeons on the highest rungs of the medical ladder, while those of the cognitive specialists and generalists lagged far behind. This was dutifully noted in the public press.

〰️

From the beginning, the chairmanship of the core in-house departments (Anesthesiology, Radiology and Pathology) had some characteristics which were different from those of the heads of clinical departments such as Surgery, Medicine or OB-Gyn:

(1) Since they started as one-physician departments, the chairman of each was responsible for assembling a team of a sufficiently large number of qualified and compatible associates to take care of the changing needs of the hospital and its medical staff, and to insure, from a professional standpoint, that the department was efficiently run, with a consistent high quality of patient care.

For awhile each also served as administrative head of the respective departments, overseeing the day-to-day operation of the entire department. Pathology was the exception; Ray Graves had asked Rufus Kervin to help him manage and operate the department from the beginning. As the departments expanded and became quite large, the administrative role has been taken over by non-physician hospital employees, now known as departmental managers or directors.

(2) To provide for stability and continuity, the chairman of the core in-house department had unlimited tenure,* as long as his service was satisfactory to the medical staff and to the hospital (and, it was presumed, as long as he had the continued support of his associates and colleagues). This was in contrast to most clinical departments, such as Medicine or Surgery,

where the chairman would serve for a term of one year.

(3) Although in-house physicians, like other members of the medical staff, were "independent contractors," not hospital employees, a written agreement was not only advisable but required by the authority to define the responsibilities and obligations of the in-house physicians and the hospital (including to each other).

The financial ground rules were: like other physicians in private practice, they were on a fee-for-service basis; that the hospital would not set the fees, but that the fee schedule must be competitive and comparable with other departments in Atlanta (the so-called "usual and customary" standard in the community) and that proposed fee raises must be formally reviewed by the hospital. All the radiologists' fees were derived from service to patients; there was no charge for supervision, no extra charges for call-back at night. The anesthesiologists, in contrast, did charge for supervision of the nurse anesthetists, who were directly responsible to them. Pathology also differed, because most of the laboratory work was not direct service to patients by the pathologists; instead, they charged for their supervision. In the case of gross or microscopic examination of tissues, which they performed themselves, their service was to patients and was charged on the fee-for-service basis.

Reflecting differences in the characteristics of the "in-house" specialties and the size of the groups, the contracts differed in some details. Over the years the hospital has at times pushed for more uniform and shorter-term contracts.

〰️

When I was selected as the radiologist, the routine proviso that "a mutually agreeable contract be worked out" was no problem. By chance I had had an unusual background of experience in hospital-radiologist relations and contracts in Georgia and even co-authored (with Glenn M. Hogan, executive director of the Georgia Hospital Association) "Recommended Guidelines for Contractual and Professional Relations Between Hospitals and Radiologists," published by the Georgia Hospital-Medical Council in 1964 (see Appendix). The fact that Taylor and members of the authority all knew me well provided the setting for frank and in-depth discussion of what I had learned:

---

*As a consequence, the chairmen of in-house departments would all serve many years on the executive committee of the medical staff (the author served 20, more than 16 of these after the hospital opened), and were in position to have a good long-range perspective.

(1) *Conflicts did not arise often, but when they did, their real nature was financial, with control a related issue.* To do their jobs well, many administrators felt the need for as much control as they could get over all aspects of the hospital operation. Hospitals always needed more money, and the contract could sometimes be used to extract some from the radiologists (and other in-house doctors).*

Radiologists wanted first-rate equipment, supplies and personnel, often straining the budget, but hospitals were not yet accustomed to spending large amounts of advances in technology even though radiology was a profit-making center. (Now radiology is a cost center and is becoming even more so.) Profit in the radiology department was counted on to reduce losses elsewhere in the hospital.

As a result, I noted, "Radiologists at times had difficulty translating their principles into economic practice, and administrators at times had difficulty translating their economic practices into principle."

(2) As the guidelines stated, *"The durability of any contract is based upon the mutual trust and respect of the hospital and the radiologist,* and the spirit of mutual cooperation with which they try to work out their common problems." Trust, the crucial ingredient, cannot be written into a contract. To be earned and sustained, it requires the qualities of honesty, the willingness to be vulnerable to a degree and appreciation of each other's problems. Where there is trust, a fairly simple contract will suffice, spelling out the mutual understanding of the working relationship, with the focus on eliminating or minimizing potential sources of conflict.

In a way, it is a pity that attorneys write hospital contracts. A hospital attorney's job is to protect the hospital, but the more he or she tries to insure that the hospital holds all the cards it needs to protect itself in all eventualities (i.e., preventing vulnerability), the more the administrator is apt to induce an adversarial climate.

I was allowed to write the first draft of the contract with Northside Hospital, and the final version, approved by the authority in July 1970, was still nominally in effect until 1992, when I formally retired. The contract (which the American Board of Radiology and I labelled an "agreement") met the criteria we relied on: there was mutual trust and confidence and the emphasis was on provisions designed to avoid future conflict.

Both Patton and Graves used it as a model for their anesthesiology and pathology contracts, modifying it to suit the needs of their own specialty department, since one size did not fit all.

As it turned out, this "ideal contract" did not prevent controversy, because (1) over time, most of the players changed,** and (2) new forces impacted hospitals throughout the country.*** The hospital argued, primarily during the 15-year tenure of the second

*In 1963, all but one of the radiologists in Georgia (who were not in medical schools or VA hospitals) were on percentage contracts; i.e. they received for their services a negotiated percentage of the total charge made by the hospital for the examination or service. Commonly this was about 35-40% of gross charges. (That sounds like a lot, but at that time a chest X-ray cost $10 and a gastrointestinal series or barium enema cost $25.) If the hospital could lower the percentage, it could keep more for itself. In 1966 and 1967, radiologists began billing for their services separately, ending this problem. But there were other ways. For example, if the insurer paid a fixed total amount for an examination or a procedure, the hospital could charge more if it induced the radiologist to charge less than usual.

Some governing boards and administrators felt all in-house physicians should ideally be salaried employees, and some of their fellow-physicians had a tinge of envy at the quasi-monopoly (or actual monopoly) aspect of their practice. At that time most physicians were in solo practice and many recalled the uncertainty, debt and financial risk they faced when they entered practice. In those days, employee benefit and other health insurance was less widespread, and the conditions of many policies required that the examinations performed or services rendered be done within a hospital; those specialists who did their work entirely in the hospital (most radiologists were hospital-based) were more likely to be paid.

**The key figure is the administrator, the player who is ordinarily on the scene for many more years than members of the authority, who rely heavily upon him for their information and perspective about what goes on in the hospital. Although he is ultimately accountable to the authority — and, in a real sense, also to the medical staff — he is usually not immediately accountable. Should he decide to exert pressure, he has a natural bully pulpit he can use at his choosing and timing. He is in position to greatly influence the reputation of any physician or group of physicians, by his personal approval or disapproval.

***Such as: (1) competition with new and other hospitals; (2) changes in U.S. government policies, including the reduction of hospital reimbursements due to the introduction of a Diagnostic-Related Group (DRG) formula in 1983. Under this system an insurer (Medicare) pays a flat fee for treatment of a particular condition, based on the average cost of treating the condition and regardless of the actual cost the patient incurs; (3) extensive and expensive advances in technology and equipment, automation and computerization, encouraging the proliferation of surgical and non-surgical, therapeutic and diagnostic, procedures and tests; (4) shift to outpatient, surgical, medical and diagnostic imaging centers; (4) growth of HMOs, PPOs and other group health provider organizations; and (5) growth of managed care, initiated by the payers as an answer to ever-rising costs.

administrator but also during the time of his successor, that times had changed and the old rules should no longer apply — especially as physicians' incomes and hospital expenses rose. One thing did not change: 25 years after the Georgia Hospital-Medical Council experience, clashes were still essentially over money and control.* (There has been no problem under the new administrator.)

In 1972 the notion floated behind the scenes that "in-house" physicians should be ineligible to serve on the hospital board, because of an inherent "conflict of interest." This blanket discrimination against a segment of the medical staff was curious, because it was said to be justified on the grounds "they might be able to bring undue influence over the board in matters pertaining to contracts or fee raises." There was no basis for this speculation; the irony was that the truth is just the opposite: no other group has less of a "conflict of interest." The welfare of the hospital-based physicians has always been directly related to, dependent on, and inseparable from Northside; no other group has a greater stake in its future.

Nevertheless, "the conflict of interest" label applied to hospital-based doctors was embraced by the second and third administrators and by some of the board, and prior to 1990 "in-house" doctors were routinely turned down with that explanation when they were occasionally nominated to the board by the medical staff's executive committee. In 1991 things changed. Now, in 1993, there are two "in-house" members, Larry Stone and John Neeld, on the board and there is another board physician, orthopedist Bill Collins, who has a business venture with the hospital. Some views die hard. An old friend of mine, a former

member of the board, still believes in-house physicians have "a conflict of interest."

It is true that any physician or layman who serves on a hospital board has a potential "conflict of interest" on any financial or other matter that may come up before the board which affects him personally or the company or group he represents. One solves this by excusing the member from decision-making (or acting as the advocate for the group represented) in the matter involved. No bank has had more financial dealings with Northside than Wachovia Bank of Georgia (formerly First National Bank of Atlanta) and it has always had members on the board since Northside began, but no one has ever seen a "conflict of interest" in that relationship.

In the mid-'60s, the majority of radiologists had percentage contracts with hospitals. In order to end conflict over the financial aspects of their relationships with hospitals and to be more like their fellow physicians (who looked down on doctors who had contracts), they switched en masse to fee-for-service charges. Percentage contracts became extinct. Almost thirty years later, their fellow physicians have also been forced to become involved, increasingly, in contracts (with healthcare payers and providers), and traditional fee-for-service medicine itself is threatened with becoming an anachronism. One consolation for the hospital-based physicians in the current epoch is that they have long had a head start over many of their fellow physicians in learning to live in the world of contracts and other practice restrictions.

---

*In one instance, involving the emergency room physicians in the early days, the hospital could not be accused of being the instigator of the quarrel. How it came about was related to the fact that the first ER physicians, unlike in the other in-house departments, were individually contracted. In 1974, Ron White, temporary spokesman for the then loosely associated group of ER physicians, initiated a ruckus over a contract proposed by the hospital by threatening a strike unless his needs and those of his colleagues (Will Murray, Tom Kennerly, James Purdy, and Gordon Peltier) were accommodated.

The chairman of the authority, Wilburn Askew, asked the chairman and vice-chairman of the medical staff, David Cohen and John Hall, for their advice. Cohen and Hall, whose practices were not yet busy, came up with a bold response. Let the ER physicians strike, they said, while Cohen, an ENT surgeon, would be responsible for assembling and providing coverage for surgical cases in the ER, and Hall, an internist and gastroenterologist, would be responsible for non-surgical care in the ER. White blinked and soon left Northside; the remainder of the ER physicians stayed. In retrospect, Hall recalls, he and Cohen were surprised by their own audacity at the time.

As a result of that episode, some members of the authority were wary of in-house physicians for a long time.

Will Murray, one of the earliest of the ER physicians, and Jim Purdy have a slightly different recall of how the events began. The financial aspect of the contract was mutually satisfactory, but according to Purdy, a collision course was inevitable because of the personality clashes of White and Chris Clark, the second administrator. Nineteen years later, Purdy and Peltier are still in practice at Northside.

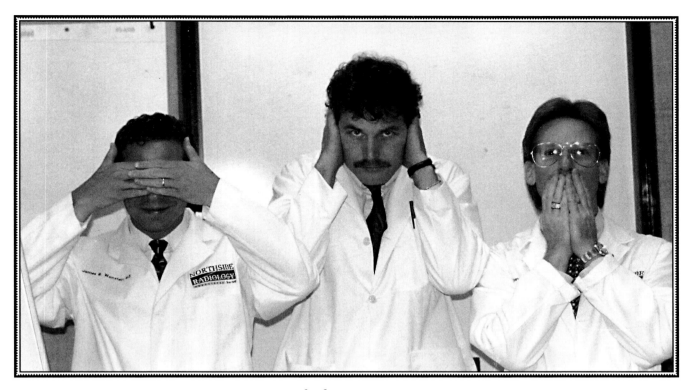

Time out for the younger generation:
Radiologists Cliff Feiner, Bob Tyrrel and Steve Citron

12

The Supporting Cast

A chaplaincy program, "entirely new in scope in hospitals in the Atlanta area," was announced to the local newspapers in May 1967 by Hollis Cobb, chairman of the authority, three years before the hospital opened. Declaring that the hospital's goal was to take care of the needs of the whole person, Cobb said that the program would provide pastoral care available at any time to those who express a desire for spiritual help.

This emerged from an organizational meeting of the Ministers Committee* to which representatives of all the churches (100, according to the papers) and synagogues (at least two) in the Northside service area were invited. The clergy were delighted at Northside's encouragement in relating religion to the healing and care-giving process, and its invitation to make substantive recommendations for the chaplaincy program as well as for a chapel, meditation rooms and office. They formed a voluntary clergy staff (with 37 active members by July 1970, when the hospital opened), with Rev. R. Denny Spear, Jr., pastor of Dunwoody Baptist Church, as president.

They agreed that the new chaplain must have "either been trained or recommended by the Georgia Association of Pastoral Care, and must have a background of several years experience in a local church ministry and also extensive training as an institutional chaplain... He will be of one of the Judeo-Christian faiths, because the vast majority of the hospital's patients is expected to come from these religious backgrounds. He is to be available for both brief and intensive counseling of patients and their families and is to have a working relationship with other clergy in the area."

The hospital initially assumed the chaplain would be a member of the hospital staff from the very first, along with the doctors and nurses. But whether due to lack of funds or to a different initial approach preferred by the clergy community who organized the clergy staff, the latter staffed the hospital with a volunteer chaplaincy program from the time the hospital opened until the first full-time chaplain, the beloved Dan E. Keels, Jr., began in 1972. Keels had come from the Baptist Hospital in Winston-Salem, recommended by Chris Clark.

A member of the clergy staff served as Chaplain of the Day each day, on call the full 24 hours, and tried to visit all newly admitted patients each day. If a patient wanted their own minister notified of their hospitalization, the chaplain made the necessary phone calls; he offered his services to those who did not have a minister.

The role of the chaplaincy at Northside has expanded over the years. In 1974, the Assistants to the Chaplain program was begun with the help of the auxiliary. The assistants have been involved in a variety of ministries, such as visiting with out-of-town patients, informing patients of the hospital chaplain's availability, calling on family members of long-term and critical patients and visiting with lonely patients at the referral of the nursing staff.

Around 1976, the department was authorized to add an associate chaplain, who would serve a two-year contract. (One of the associate chaplains, Larry

*Rev. Gerald Jacobson, pastor of the North Springs Methodist Church, served as temporary chairman. The meeting began with an address by Dr. Charles Gerkin, director of the Chaplaincy Program at Grady Hospital and executive director of the Georgia Association of Pastoral Care.

(l-r): Rev. Gerald Jackson, Dr. Charles Gerkin, and Hollis Cobb

Connelly, subsequently became the first chaplain at Piedmont Hospital; another, Jerry Gardner, became the first at Shepherd Spinal Center.)

The department became associated with the Clinical Pastoral Education program directed by Chaplain Imogene Bennett at Scottish Rite, and Bennett began assigning two basic CPE students each quarter to do their clinical work (visitation with hospitalized patients) at Northside.

In 1989, two months after Keels was diagnosed as having a malignant brain tumor, a resident CPE student, Charles Passman, from the Scottish Rite program, was assigned to Northside. Keels died in December. (Northside's chapel, which was originally dedicated to the memory of Luke Swensson, has been renamed in his honor.) In August 1989, when Passman completed his residency, he was hired by Northside as associate chaplain and soon the popular Passman took over as director of Pastoral Care.

Shortly, both Northside and St. Joseph's became part of a Tri-Hospital CPE program with Scottish Rite, and in 1990, Northside hired Gene Locke, a full-time CPE supervisor/associate chaplain, for its CPE program.

Jayne Howard has been secretary of the Chaplaincy Department for 18 years. One of her many duties is to notify churches and synagogues of their members' admission to Northside.

〰〰

The auxiliary also had an early start. Almost 30 months before the hospital opened, the medical staff, through its chairman Jud Hawk, reported to the authority that it wanted to push ahead to establish a Women's Auxiliary for the hospital. The authority insisted on waiting until the administrator, Joe Taylor, was hired, but then quickly gave its blessing.

During 1968, Tully Blalock, one of the two physician members on the authority and chairman of its Public Relations Committee, talked with a number of women, some of whom directed him to Mrs. Matthew (Ellen) Dwyer, Counselor for the Georgia State

Hospital Association Women's Auxiliary and president of St. Joseph's Hospital Auxiliary.

She agreed to recruit a group of prominent, interested area residents. On March 19, 1969, she and five other women met with Taylor, Blalock and Keith Quarterman, the new chairman of the medical staff, to discuss the purpose and needs of the auxiliary. Each of the women agreed to contact five more potential members to attend an organizational meeting in April. In fact, 27 women became charter members* at that meeting.

The recruits were more than enthusiastic and the group soon snowballed. Coffees were held in private homes; general meetings were held in the Lenox Square Auditorium. Uniforms were ordered and a local church allowed its facility to be used for service orientations while the hospital was still under construction. The first in-service to the hospital was staffing the information desk — directing salesmen, suppliers and others to work areas — before the hospital opened. On the day Northside officially opened, June 27, 1970, there was a 292-member auxiliary, 100 of whom were in full uniform for the ribbon cutting.

The "Pink Ladies" became known as the "Auxilians" in August 1972, when male volunteers were approved for membership. (For more about the auxiliary, see appendix.)

wwww

Taylor assembled his small but eager key administrative staff:

Rita Engelhardt was in charge of Nursing Services and Patient Care. A former nun, she had held several posts as hospital administrator, most recently

*Frances Shipman Adams, Virginia Bastedo, Doris Bobbitt, Loretta Bruce, Maxine Buckingham, Anne Casey, Jean Durden, Ellen Dwyer, Candee Elrod, Rosemary Fox, Elizabeth Fry, Ann Hendrix, Charlotte Hunt, Kitty Jackson, Betty Kerr, Mary Louise McCoy, Louise McGuire, Marian Moody, Colleen Norman, Grace Robertson, Vonnie Rossman, Chastain Schoen, Rosemary Smither, Mrs. J.D. Stone, Jane Vantress, Virginia Walters and Betty Weaver.

Administrator Joe Taylor (r) and Associate Administrator George Landsdell ready for hospital opening.

at Holy Family Hospital in Atlanta for five years. She was subsequently described as "very bright and very dedicated, but a bit ethereal in her thinking." She said that a nurse had three main duties: "She must be comforting by conveying a source of strength and by relieving physical pain and emotional stress; she must be very keen in observing changes of condition in order to inform the doctor; and she must become an educator to her patients by being able to explain scientific concepts in terms they can understand. The nurse must be someone on whom the patient can unload some of his or her apprehensions and must be a good listener and an excellent communicator."

George Lansdell, red-haired associate administrator and chief financial officer, was previously at a hospital in Bainbridge, Georgia in the same capacity. He came highly recommended by two of Taylor's peer administrators. Lansdell, who was intrigued by the brave new world of computers, was knowledgeable but somewhat stubborn.

Bill Roberts, in charge of Personnel, including Employee Assessment and Employee Health, was a former union office manager and a friend of mental health's Dr. Charles Edwards. Due to the hospital's lack of funds, he had to postpone hiring until as late as possible before the scheduled opening. Liberal in his hiring policies, he encouraged diversity, and sometimes was more influenced by applicants' promise and enthusiasm than by their submitted record of skills. He said there would be no supervisors on the staff, only coordinators, because "at Northside, people are not supervised; they are coordinated."

Ken Dykes was the first controller.

Niles Travell, a compulsive systems analyst, worked behind the scenes with multiple tasks — (at one time, in charge of the Business Office), Medical Records, Admissions and the implementation of a new concept, the Service Control Center. I do not know who came up with the idea of the soon controversial SCC (which was supposed to keep track — in one place — of all doctors' orders and "process the physical flow of patient care through the hospital"), but it was a doozy.

The Trustees of the

Northside Hospital Association

and

The Hospital Authority of Fulton County

Cordially invite you to

The Dedication of the New Northside Hospital

Saturday, June 27, 2 P. M.

Guest Speaker: Senator Herman Talmadge

The Dedication will be followed by an

Open House and Tours

Saturday, June 27, 3 P. M. to 6 P. M.

Sunday, June 28, 2 P. M. to 7 P. M.

Please come

Show Time

At the dedication ceremony* on Saturday June 27, the public was welcomed by Archie Lindsey, the popular former county commissioner who succeeded Hollis Cobb as chairman of the Hospital Authority. U.S. Senator Herman Talmadge, the principal speaker, blasted the Vietnam anti-war amendments that the Senate had been debating for six weeks as "little more than an exercise in futility." But the public was much more interested in exploring their long-awaited "$8.5 Million Innovative Facility," and during two days of open house and public tours (with 100 uniformed Pink Ladies stationed at 38 areas in the hospital), an estimated 10,000 people toured the hospital, according to Grizzard and Haas, the firm which handled the arrangements for the luncheon and program and worked with the hospital staff and Auxiliary in preparing for the tours.

*Rabbi Richard Lehrman of the Temple Sinai delivered the invocation; the Reverend Douglas C. Turley, St. Patrick's Episcopal Church, dedicated the hospital, and the benediction was delivered by Father John Kiernan, Church of St. Jude the Apostle.

From The Atlanta Journal, *June 23, 1970*

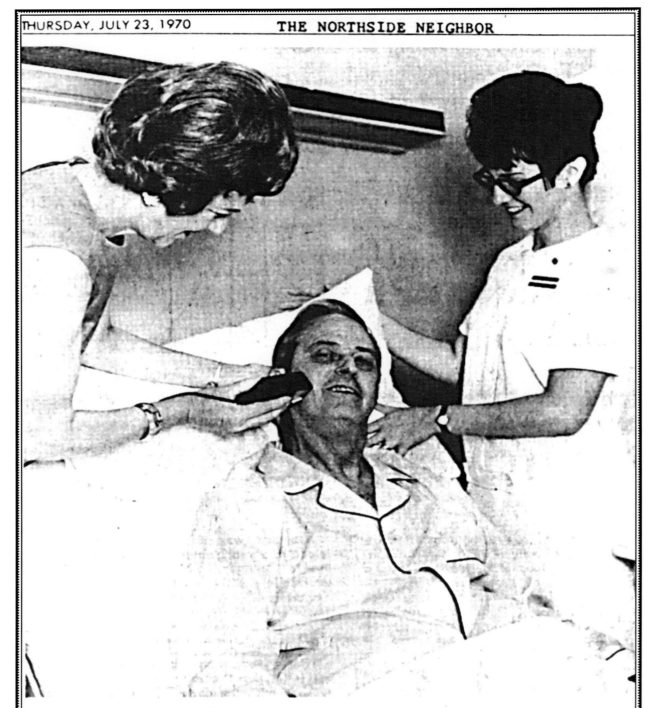

Special Care for First Patient

J.E. Carroll, the first patient at the newly opened Northside Hospital, receives special care from nurse Betty Maris and wife Florence. Carroll and his wife, residents of the northeast Atlanta, have two children. The hospital which opened July 6, offers microwave ovens, family rooms and an admissions system where all details are handled in the patient's room.

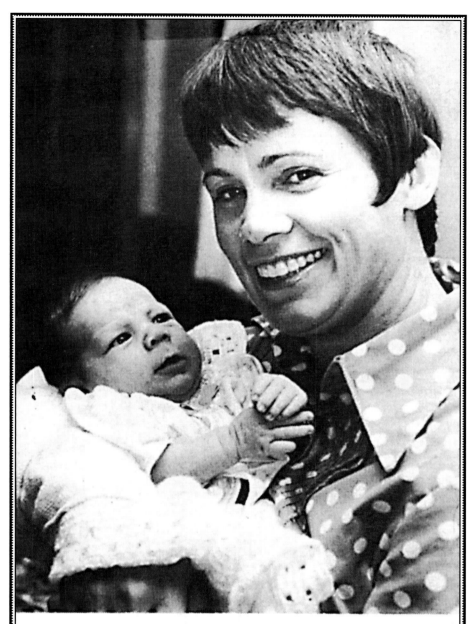

His Parents' Third Son

Mrs. Leo Sekula of Hampton Hill Drive N.E., holds her new son, Robert Leo, who has the distinction of being the first baby born at the new Northside Hospital. The infant was born on July 27 at 3:24 p.m. and weighed 7 lbs., 11½ oz. He is his parents' third son.

Leo Sekula: the first baby born at Northside.

Rufus Kervin, the director of the laboratory, was struck by the fact that at least one-third of the numerous visitors to his section were pregnant women.

Alice Wofford (her maiden name was Mister), hired as a clerk in the business office, didn't make it to the ribbon-cutting ceremony because she was too busy hunting envelopes. Someone had forgotten to buy envelopes for mailing bills. "I looked around and realized that I and one other girl were the business office. And she quit after one day."

These two anecdotes provide a prophetic glimpse into the near future. But everyone was prepared to deal with a first year when it would take a while for things to run smoothly and predictably, for Northside was a barely completed physical plant in which none of the administrative staff nor the remainder of the hospital employees, including nurses, had ever worked together before.

F I R S T S

The first admitted patient: J.E. Carroll, a patient of internist Thorne Winter. At least, he was the first "first patient" whose picture appeared in the newspapers.* (One scrapbook named Sara Hudson as the first admitted patient, and someone thought surgeon Ben Thebaut might have admitted the first patient, but initially no log book was kept on admissions, so there is no written record.)

The first out-patient: Mrs. Jean Durden, was the first patient to have lab work performed, before the hospital even officially opened. A charter member of the auxiliary, she has served as its president.

The first delivery: Robert Leo, the third son of Mrs. Leo Sekula, was born on July 27, and delivered by Dr. Herbert Shessel.

The first operating room supervisor: Mary Lou Riley. She left after a few years when her husband was transferred, but returned to work at Northside in 1989 or 1990.

The first evening house coordinator: June Chastain. She has been at Northside since day one. Her classic early days recollection: "We had our ups and downs, but we had a unique experience — the opportunity to work with the best at the best!"

The first night house coordinator: Frances Purtyman.

The first pharmacy nurse: Shirley Kinnard. Vivian Gay was coordinator of the Pharmacy Nurses Program.

---

*Bill Roberts gives an amusing, different version: "I was responsible for public relations. We had made arrangements with all the newspapers to publicize the first patient we had, and we all sat around eagerly, waiting for the hospital to open. Our first patient was a man who had a relatively severe industrial injury; he certainly was not suitable to be publicized. Our second patient was admitted to the Mental Health center; this was confidential and could not be publicized. Our third, who was in for Labor and Delivery, by default became the first patient for our purposes."

14

*The First Year: Supergrowth,
Frustrations, Empowerment*

The first six months turned out to be even more volatile than expected.

The hospital opened in stages. The first, on July 6, was a combined Medical-Surgical floor* of 44 beds. Two weeks later the 32-bed obstetrical service opened. By September 1 the OB area was jammed tight. They were literally parking mothers in the hallway outside the maternity area, and many mothers had to be kept in the labor and delivery area after delivery because there were no beds.

The emergency area was also quickly overrun, following its July 1 opening, with over 50,000 visits the first year. The five ER slots were small and crowded. The ER entrance was not easy for patients, policemen or ambulance drivers to find, since there were still no signs to indicate the presence of a hospital nearby and there was no off-ramp from the expressway. The ER was the only one in this part of metropolitan Atlanta, however, and the scene inside was sometimes chaotic.

"Med-Surg" also picked up quickly, and on August 1 the second of the four patient floors opened.** By the end of 1970 the hospital was fully operational.

When the hospital first opened, there was no recovery room, no intensive care unit (ICU) and no coronary care unit (CCU).*** "Float" nurses were borrowed from the ER as needed, day or night, to take care of patients who had been operated upon.

The overall census rose in January, and in early 1971 the hospital was running at 85-90% capacity (bed occupancy) and stayed that way the entire time Taylor was at Northside — except for OB, which stayed at a crisis level constantly. The mental health-psychiatric unit of 25 beds also had a fairly high level of occupancy.

As it immediately became evident that Northside was revolutionizing OB care in the Atlanta area, and OB patients began coming from further distances — Athens, Cartersville, towns in west Georgia, etc. — the obstetricians (Shessel, Spanier, Kahle, and Saul Vitner among others) and Taylor were convinced that major changes were needed to take care of the increasing load and their commitment to a first-rate obstetrical service. They (principally, Kahle and Earl Hathcock) sat down with the architects from the firm of Abreu and Robeson and sketched plans for a separate maternity pavilion to be built between the doctors' parking lot and a projected nursing home.

In hospital circles at that time maternity services were considered unprofitable, particularly at the size they existed in most hospitals. Although

---

*This was the first of four patient floors of the same size which towered above the two main hospital levels. As previously noted, Labor & Delivery was located on the ground floor, Postpartum and Nursery were on the second floor.

**These first two floors were immediately rearranged, with one floor exclusively for surgery and one for medicine. On October 1, the next top floor was opened, and exactly two months later the final (sixth) floor was opened, including a pediatric and adolescent section.

***The ICU opened in September and the CCU in December, under the direct supervision of Bill Eyzaguirre, who had just completed a cardiac residency at Piedmont Hospital. "Ace" was hired by the hospital to get these units going, and had helped select the equipment and train his personnel. Enthusiastic, reliable, and relatively unflappable, he spent so much of his time in the hospital that he was an unofficial "in-house cardiologist," a welcome roving consultant in acute emergencies in the ER and elsewhere. (For a time he officially read all the electrocardiograms obtained in the hospital.)

Northside was short of funds, Taylor and the obstetricians were convinced that a maternity pavilion at Northside was not only a financially sound idea (high quality required high volume and vice versa), but that this would serve to induce north Atlanta families to use Northside for the rest of their medical care, and to cement the relationship with the patients who had already been to Northside.

The more the idea was discussed, the more it was recognized that this was a piecemeal solution, involving only one of the hospital's space problem areas. Within six months the hospital began planning a major addition of 150 beds, redesigning the maternity service and converting the maternity floor to further Med-Surg beds. (Actual building did not occur until two years later.)

wwww

The certainty of early expansion prompted other specialists to bombard Joe Taylor with recommendations, some of which were creative and long-range in conception. Orthopedist Warner Wood begged Taylor to consider the early construction of an orthopedic tower, devoted to orthopedic surgery and ancillary facilities, which, he guaranteed Taylor, would be completely filled and utilized in no time flat, and would be a great boon to Northside and to Atlanta.*

wwww

Taylor not only had to open the hospital without any funds to meet the payroll and other operating expenses until an accounts-receivable cash flow arrived; in fact, he had negative working capital, since several hundred thousand dollars were owed to vendors for equipment and supplies requested by the medical staff and bought shortly before the hospital opened. The vendors knew the hospital's financial situation (Taylor was quite frank with them), but they had confidence in Northside's success. Most, like American Hospital Supply and Baxter Laboratories, were willing to carry the account month after month, shipping everything that was ordered. Gradually they were all paid.

On paper the hospital made a profit the third month after opening, but there was no positive cash flow for six to eight months because there were major glitches in organizing the IBM computer system for billing and systematizing the office procedure which took about eight months to overcome.**

As a result, the business office was a disaster zone: accounts receivable was in total disarray, most bills were not sent out on a regular basis for six months or more, and the set-up made it difficult to handle claims with insurance companies and third-party payers. Taylor remembers that period as "a living hell."

I recall several instances of being stopped on the street, at a social gathering or called on the phone by friends and/or neighbors who had been patients at Northside, asking that I exert any influence I might have as head of Radiology to help them get a bill from Northside so that they could pay it. In January 1971 the business office's Alice Mister persuaded several personnel and their spouses to spend three to four hours a night for a solid week stuffing bills into envelopes to help end the billing debacle.

---

*Wood was right in his assessment, but this was the wrong time and, for this hospital, the wrong era for such a good "business" decision. For, even if Northside were not in a financial hole that first year, it is unlikely that it would have given this project a high priority. More than a decade prior to the rise of the government-encouraged entrepreneurial approach to medicine, the medical-industrial complex, and marketing ("when medicine became a commodity and no longer a service"), hospitals spent their money conservatively, and usually expanded slowly and cautiously, to meet needs which clamored for attention. It was unlikely that a hospital authority, with its government sponsorship implying the highest degree of fiduciary responsibility, would single out orthopedics for special attention, in order to encourage future growth, when there were more immediate concerns to be met. Of course, in those days it was easier to be fiscally responsible, since there was no competition.

Wood, whose primary office was downtown, had been a member of the steering committee of the Northside Hospital Association in its first year (1962), but he lost interest the following year, when the hospital site in then far-off Sandy Springs was selected, and until after it was built, seven years later. He had been convinced Buckhead would have been a better location. Now he smiles, "So much for my foresight." By the time he decided to move to The Hill, Northside had a sufficiency of orthopedists and Wood was one of those who would practice full-time across the street at St. Joseph's, where there is now a sports medicine center, which is one of that hospital complex's major attractions.

**Like other employees in the business office, the key-punch operators were hired late, poorly trained and not properly supervised, and the software programs did not function satisfactorily. There was only a one-week run-through of the business operation before the hospital opened. A batch processing system was in effect, with several hospitals taking turns sharing the use of the IBM System 30 (32K capacity), which ran 24 hours a day.

In early 1971, a financial crisis was averted when the treasurer of the authority, Eugene Adams of the First National Bank, through his superiors, Wilburn Askew and Andy Huber, arranged a loan of one million dollars from his parent bank. It wasn't easy — none of the other banks would take the risk. It was his proudest achievement in his 17-year association with Northside.*

Gene, a long-time member and one-time chairman of the board of trustees of the Northside Hospital Association, was not eligible to be a full-fledged voting member of the hospital authority of Fulton County because he lived in DeKalb. He served for 10 years as ex-officio treasurer of the authority. (He was elected tax commissioner of DeKalb County and served for 20 years, until he retired in 1992.)

Meanwhile, Niles Travell, the systems analyst who had also been in the business operation, had quit out of frustration, and George Lansdell, the associate administrator and CFO, left before the end of 1970. After this shake-down period, and the loan boost, the business office came under control and according to Taylor, the loan was completely paid off by the end of 1971.

〰️

"When you're up to your ass in alligators, it's hard to remember that your first objective was to drain the swamp." AUTHOR UNKNOWN

Despite the distractions and frustrations during that first six to eight months, Northside never wavered from its intense focus on providing a new, high level in patient care.

During Gene Adams' solicitation of funds for Northside, he approached Ted Faber, an ex-Air Force pilot from California, who was an aerospace safety engineer at Lockheed. Ted responded, "I haven't any money, I have two boys in college, but you can have my wife — she's a nurse." Emmy-lou, a nurse at Emory, volunteered her services, and prior to the opening of the hospital, helped set up the ER, unpacked instruments in the OR, and did other assorted chores. She was reluctant to work full-time (she still had a small child at home), but she was so good at everything she did** that, four weeks after the hospital opened, she was persuaded to become its long-time Director of Education.

To people like her and Rufus Kervin, manager of the Laboratory Services, Northside's working atmosphere that Joe Taylor and others set up was marvelous, heady stuff. She had come from Emory, where, at that time, policies and procedures, rules and protocol, set forth in great detail, seemed to have been fixed in place for a hundred years; and Kervin had come to Northside after working under the stiffly hierarchal, strictly regulated Army system. In Kervin's cherished memory, "Taylor's manner and ability to empower employees — ahead of his time — to take charge and do things on their own, were characteristics needed for this phase of the hospital ... a key factor in getting 200, 300, then 400 people, in a short period of time, to work together as a team."

Faber recalled, "Everyone was assigned their responsibility and was expected to do it. And if you made a mistake, you picked yourself up, brushed yourself off, and re-did whatever it was. Of course, if you made the same mistake twice, you were in a fair amount of difficulty. But this ability to proceed on your own to the goals you were given, we now know in management circles, does get the most and best work from people, when you are treated as though you do have a brain."

In the beginning there was some territory guarding, as each area had its hands full trying to "hit the ground running" and optimize its own operation,

---

*Adams was followed on the authority by other executive vice-presidents of the First National Bank. First, Julian Barfield, then by Wilburn Askew, Thomas Hills and William Deyo, Jr. Askew and Hills served terms as chairman of the authority, and Deyo is currently chairman of the hospital board, which is now a separate entity under a 1991 restructuring.

The First National Bank of Atlanta is now known as the Wachovia Bank of Georgia. Its recent chairman, Raymond Riddle, has also been a long-time personal supporter of Northside and chaired one of the later fund-raising campaigns, along with the author. Symbolic of the continuous support the bank has given Northside since 1963, he was named Honorary Chairman of the 1992 Northside Ball, sponsored by the Northside Foundation. In late 1992 he changed jobs, taking the place of Sidney Kirschner, who had been president and CEO of National Service Industries, a conglomerate based in Atlanta. This was soon after Kirschner, a member of Northside's authority for eight years, had left NSI to become Northside's new Administrator and CEO.

**The assessment that Emmy-lou was a woman for all seasons proved correct, and eighteen years later the Auxiliary gave a special award to "The Nurse Who Made the Difference."

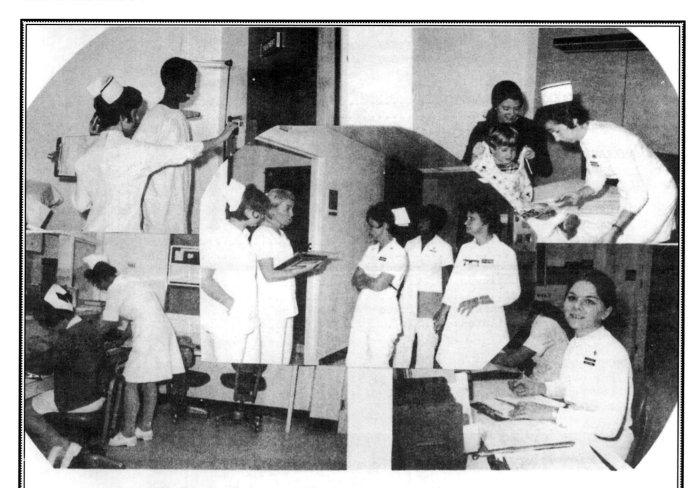

TEAM NURSING

The aim of team nursing is getting to know the patient, finding out and understanding all of his unique needs. As a team leader team conferences are very enlightening. These conferences give each member of the team the opportunity to discuss the patient's specific needs and how to meet them. The nurse in charge of the nursing team must also try to understand the needs of her co-workers in order to produce a well-coordinated and harmonious team.

Team nursing is working together as a whole. R.N.s and N.A.s working together as a coordinating team, each knowing their responsibility and fulfilling it to the best of their ability.

This page is from "The Thing," an amateurish but enthusiastic in-hospital newsletter which appeared soon after Northside opened in 1970 and lasted a few issues.

THE FIRST ONE HUNDRED YEARS ARE THE HARDEST

By Roberta Hiscock

"You're telling ME 1060 babies have been delivered here!!!"

"Do you think Joe Taylor seems to have aged a little!"

OUR FIRST SIX MONTHS

- FREE PARKING FOR EMPLOYEES

"They're replacing the bed pan washers... HOW CLEVER!!!"

"I like mini skirts, myself!"

Pant suits allow the nurse more freedom of movement.

"How long was that, elevator hung between floors?"

"SCC who?"

"That 'whiz' tube system is on the blink again!!!"

"Twenty down - Eighty to go!"

These drawings were done after Northside had been open six months by recruiter **Roberta** Hiscock who works in the Human Resources Division. Roberta has been an employee of Northside since early June, 1970. Many employees in the beginning did various jobs and Roberta frequently helped us look at the funny side of our "trials".

Some of the cartoons apply today. We did have S.C.C. which was a central cleaning house for all doctors orders. The worried M.D. in the cartoon never made it to the first year anniversary. We did have parking gates so close (to make room for more spaces) that "big cars" couldn't get through them.

Let's never go back to the "good ole' days"!

*Reprinted from January 1971, Volume I, Number 5 issue of the Pacemaker

but this was understandable since time and energy were limited.*

During the summer and early fall months many would work 12 to 14 hours a day, with no time off — and a pay check that did not arrive on time every month. Some managers did not get paid for one to two months at a time. But this was no big problem, since many expected it and took it in stride, knowing there was no turning back and believing they were on the right road. They were on a campaign high.

Most of the support staff, hired no earlier than June 29 because the hospital had no funds to pay them, were new to the hospital world and the few with experience spent time orienting the recruits. Alice Mister recalled, "The hospital was willing to hire people from the community, but nobody knew what they were doing. Girls who had just graduated from high school were helping out with purchasing. Some were helping route doctors' 'orders.' Once, a doctor hit the ceiling because his request for an 'electrolyte package' (a group of laboratory tests) on one of his patients went unanswered. The request had been routed to the maintenance department, instead of the lab, since it sounded something like 'electric light.' We finally got our act together, and it was very satisfying to see a little part of it fall into place each day."

A major obstacle at that time was that there was no public transportation. (MARTA buses would not arrive in the area until 1973.) Bill Roberts, the first personnel manager, tells it like it was: "It was very difficult for us to get nursing assistants and housekeeping personnel (maids, janitors, orderlies) because there was no bus service to the hospital, and we were having trouble finding qualified people, even if we were willing to pay more than hospitals in other areas. So it became obvious to us that, if we were going to be able to staff our hospital as quickly as needed, we were going to have to train our own entry level employees. We took basically untrained people and taught them how to reliably do blood pressures, bed pan duties, take temperatures — just some very minor stuff to help the nursing staff — and put them to work. We made a tremendous, tremendous request to the Medical Staff that they be patient with us while we trained these people to the confidence level that both we and the medical staff expected them to be.

"Unfortunately, many physicians were not very tolerant of our efforts; they expected highly trained and competent employees. Some of the doctors were so harsh on our untrained entry level employees that a number of employees would just walk away and leave their job and not even come in and pick up their paycheck. At one time there were 50 final checks for employees that we were holding because they never came back to pick up their last check. We created a whole new category of termination called 'abandoning your job.' Fortunately, this problem, too, went away quickly because the nursing staff, many of the doctors, in fact, everybody, became intensely interested in getting these people trained."

To make the first year more trying, a nursing shortage was developing in Atlanta and around the country. Generally, jobs were plentiful in this country at that time, nurses' pay was low, and other options became more appealing. The large, increasing number of physicians now practicing in the northside area siphoned off some of the nurses who lived in the area and who had their own transportation, because the physician could afford to pay more to a nurse in his private office than the hospital could offer. In addition, due to the financial crunch of the first six months, the hospital was able to afford only part of the number of nurses needed, and for a time had to rely upon a larger proportion of nursing assistants than it had ever contemplated. By September, three months after opening, there was difficulty in acquiring sufficient nurses to staff the newly opened floors.

"One very interesting thing — if there was anything new in health care, Northside tried it," recalled Faber, who had been a nurse for 20 years. When she arrived to work part-time in the ER as a "floater," covering for other nurses elsewhere in the hospital, she

---

*Early on, coordination and communication between different groups of employees suffered because of their differing backgrounds. Some had learned how to do things in different ways or under different rules, and some, emboldened by "empowerment," made it up as they went along. As a result, the left hand was not always aware of what the right hand was doing:

The lab manager was promised by a vendor that an expensive piece of equipment would arrive by opening day. After repeated calls, the vice-president of the company personally delivered the equipment, with apologies. Having done so, he pointed out that the equipment had already been delivered three times, but Northside's purchasing agent would not allow the equipment to be left because it was delivered after a certain time. (The purchasing agent had a rule that deliveries could not be made after a certain hour, but the lab had never been made aware of it.)

was surprised that there were no policy and procedure books, no cardexes (the "nurse's right arm," a file of cards containing specific patient orders and instructions copied by a clerk from the patient's chart) and no head nurses ("team nursing" instead). This was by intent.

The rationale of eliminating the cardex was to insure that the nurse would have to look directly at the patient's chart to find the doctor's orders, thereby eliminating inaccuracies which could be made by a clerk or secretary transferring a written copy of the order to the cardex. But it often took a lot of a nurse's time to find the chart (which might be in the hands of a physician or another nurse at the time, or which might have been moved from its usual location for other reasons), and nurses were at a premium, so far as the hospital's budget was concerned. Result: a high frustration level for nurses.

"Team nursing" was a newly recommended concept in taking care of patients. Teams of nurses, with nursing assistants under their supervision, were assigned to different wings of the hospital. But the physician was often burdened with having to track down the different team leaders in contrast to the old system, where he could talk with one head nurse about his patients.

These modifications did not work well in the real world,* and with gentle but firm prodding by some of the nurses and physicians, the "tried and true" ways were quickly restored, particularly in the critical care areas.

Emmy-lou laughs at the memory of the TV Camera Episode. "Each of the 44-bed nursing units had a TV camera on the desk where you sat with a machine, prepared to answer a patient's call button. It was designed so that the patient on his (or her) monitor could see the real person who was answering the call, and it would, it was hoped, give the patients the feeling of more personal attention, knowing they could see who was smiling at them and caring for their needs. In the beginning, when we had Pink Ladies in the reception area, they would answer the patient's call button, but they were very self-conscious and did not like being on TV. Later, when

the auxiliary was more needed elsewhere, or on the evening shift or at night — when it was only the nurse who answered the call button — all the patients ever saw was the stomach of a nurse. Since she never had time to sit down, she would just lean over and ask the patients what they wanted. Those TV cameras were removed. It was a great idea, but they never did accomplish their purpose."

The reverse use of TV was seemingly foolproof: the two end rooms on the east and west wings were equipped with reverse cameras so that the sickest patients could be put in these rooms, easily watched over the TV monitor by nurse(s) at the nursing station. This use of TV worked too well; it was felt by some to be too much of an invasion of privacy, and it was soon discontinued.

Two pharmacy innovations were instantly and widely appreciated: the unit dosage system of dispensing medications and the practice of having pharmacy nurses administering medications to patients at bedside, with every bottle labelled at the point of use. Medication errors were almost nil, in contrast to other hospitals in Atlanta and around the country. The physicians were grateful and laudatory, and this quickly became one of Northside's several attractive drawing cards. The pharmacy itself, managed by Jimmy Setzer,** was initially tiny, described by some as a "hip pocket operation," but that did not affect its service.

Bill Roberts, who now has a consulting firm in Greenville, S.C., has bittersweet memories of 1970-71 at Northside. He was hired by Joe Taylor in the management crew "basically because I had some exposure to unions and unionization activities, and at that time there was some concern that Local 1199 was interested in organizing hospital workers in Atlanta. My charge was to develop a set of personnel policies that virtually would ensure as much as humanly possible that hospital employees would not feel the need to join a labor union." Roberts says that, "The policies we developed were not really mine; the entire management team (including Dr. Charles Edwards, chief of Mental Health) developed the personnel policies of the hospital.

---

*The concept of team nursing was abandoned too quickly. Joe Taylor said later, "We tried to make too many innovations, and all at the same time." Currently, in the 1990s, it has been revisited and reincarnated as one of the features under the label and umbrella of "Patient Focused Care."

**Setzer had been the pharmacist at the LaGrange hospital where Taylor had been the previous administrator. There, thirteen years earlier, Camilla Myhand had initiated these innovations.

"The management staff meetings were usually very intense, very forceful and sometimes very loud. Everyone was free to voice their opinions, and they would argue with each other. But, when the meeting was over, they would all be in agreement as to what would be done and how they were going to do it." Rita Engelhardt came into Roberts' office one day and said she could not understand how they could all sit and argue and fuss with other and still be friends and work together. But somehow they did.

Roberts remembers the first snow and ice storm as a very traumatic event, since the hospital was caught by surprise and did not have a good procedure or contingency plan for getting personnel to work. A huge number of Labor and Delivery patients came in early, anticipating difficulty getting into the hospital during the ice storm. With an overload of patients and very few staff people, virtually everyone was drafted to be a patient care employee. Roberts worked in the ER, checking blood pressure and vital signs and getting medical histories. If the floor needed mopping, the administrative team was not averse to pitching in. That experience, everyone working closely together, regardless of rank or position, served as a valuable stimulus. Roberts said, "Everyone who worked there knew and understood what was expected of them, and our employees were one of the most competent group of employees anywhere. Some of the things we did became models for other local hospitals."

Roberts wrote me, "I must tell you that dictating my memories was more difficult than I imagined it would be. My emotions about Northside have deeper roots than I realized. The most important thing we did was develop a degree of caring and teamwork that was unique in hospitals at that time* and, I think, is impossible with the new MBA type management style that followed Joe Taylor."

In press releases from the time construction began until the hospital opened, Northside had promised the public not only the "latest word in hospital facilities" but the effort to make it as oriented to the patient's convenience as possible. The most publicized claim — "an admission system where all details are handled in the patient's room" — turned out to be only a partial success, requiring more personnel and personnel time (and, therefore, more hospital expense) than anticipated. An admissions office was subsequently opened, but the convenience concept was welcomed by patients, and a year later 75% of all patients were able to bypass the admissions office. These patients were "pre-admitted" by having their physician call the hospital to notify them of the patient's arrival, after which a staff member would contact the patient's family.

The "cookless kitchen" concept (microwave ovens on each floor, using nothing but convenience precooked food, obviating the need for cooks and dishwashing equipment, and minimizing the number of kitchen employees, etc.) was too simplistic to meet the needs and the palates of most hospital patients and wound up displeasing almost everyone.

First of all, in 1970 microwaves were still something of a novelty, there were relatively few in homes in this country, and the selection and quality of commercially available frozen foods was limited. This would change, but not fast enough.

Equally obvious was that many hospital patients required special (low-salt, etc.) or bland diets, and it was difficult for the kitchen to come up with anything but a "regular diet." (Since they were young and healthy and in the hospital only briefly, the obstetrical patients tolerated the "regular diet" of prepackaged, pre-cooked foods better than any other group.) Although this approach required tremendous refrigerator and freezing areas, there was not much cooking facility, and there was no flexibility. Also, patients were not always ready to be served at the time the freshly microwaved food arrived, and re-zapping the food diminished its palatability.

---

*"The kind of openness," Roberts continued, "the kind of team atmosphere we had, may have been one of the most dynamic employee development systems, I think, ever seen in a hospital. We had some people who came in and developed skills they did not know they had and they became nationally recognized for their competence.

"When I hired Alice (Wofford) Mister, she was a housewife just looking for something to do. She came to work in a simple clerical function. She worked hard and was promoted to office manager. That was probably a little too much for her, but she later became manager of Admissions, where she excelled. She received national publicity for the work that she did in Admissions. Alice was not an isolated case. One gentleman, who started as a nursing assistant in the Mental Health Center, went on to become a business executive. In its early days, Northside had the ability to take people and give them the expectation of excellence, but at the same time let them know that they had the freedom to develop to their full potential, and most of our employees took advantage of that."

From the standpoint of the "bottom-line" business manager, it certainly was not cost-effective. It cut down on the number of kitchen employees, but it took up the more valuable time of nurses (who were already up to their eyeballs in patient care), the pre-packaged or pre-cooked foods were not inexpensive, and the heavy use of disposables helped glut the trash removal system.

Those who were not dissatisfied by the microwaved meals had another opportunity to be offended — by the meal schedule. The hospital opened serving five meals a day, and did so for a year, under the direction of the chief dietitian, Ladelle Snyder. The meal service looked good on paper:

6:00-6:30 A.M. (before lab tests) Continental breakfast
9:30 A.M. Regular breakfast
11:30 A.M. Lunch (usually sandwiches and salad)
4:30 P.M. Proper dinner
8:00-8:30 P.M. Snack

It took a tremendous amount of expensive nursing time to serve these meals, and many patients felt they had no time to catch their breath. They were involved with lab tests or radiology or some surgical or other procedure or with visitors, and felt they had little time for catnaps or rest.

The hospital worked with the system for well over a year; it was difficult to get the dietitian to change it. At great expense the kitchen was refitted. Major renovation did not occur until 1974-75, at the time of hospital expansion, with a much larger cooking area, and some of the freezers were taken out.

The "cookless kitchen" was supposed to eliminate the necessity for a dishwasher since everything would be disposable, including bottles and trays. In fact, the hospital opened in the Disposable Age. Sheets, gowns, even some surgical instruments —

attention was focused on how many ways disposables could be used. They appeared to be convenient, saved time and helped keep the hospital clean. In addition to their expense, however, they contributed mightily to the trash which had to be disposed of each day.

How to get rid of all this garbage? The hospital had an answer: the Great Garbage Compactor. This "odorless, pollution-free waste disposal system,* designed to compact and sanitize 15 pounds of waste per patient per day" was the first of its kind in the Atlanta area. The hospital engineer, John Johnston, said the hospital was able to get "at least 10 times as much" processed garbage into a dumpster as "regular old garbage."

The idea was terrific, but the basement compactor, where the chewed-up trash was mixed with water, very often plugged up. This part of the basement also housed Central Supply, Pharmacy, Fiscal Affairs, the Mail Room and Flower Delivery — which intermittently had to put up with a terrible stench. Finally, the entire thing was ripped out because it could not be kept consistently operational, and the hospital went back to the old, conventional system where the bagged trash was pulled by hand to the dumpster. (The dumpster is still used both for linen drop and trash.)

As the last six months of 1970 sped by, many of the physicians** were also becoming increasingly frustrated. They had expected the hospital to be a little disorganized at the beginning but, for them, things seemed to be getting no better each month. Ironically, patients were receiving on the whole very good care, but only because of the extraordinary amount of time, effort and dedication of almost everyone connected with the hospital, not the least of which were the physicians themselves.***

*All waste products were bagged and deposited in a gravity chute on each of the seven floors of the hospital, landing in a closed room in the basement which contained a pulping machine. (Negative air pressure drew air into the open chute door, eliminating cross contamination from "puff-back.") With its giant shears this pulping unit would convert "just about any kind of garbage — tin cans, cardboard, rubber tubing, etc." — into a fine pulp in a germicidal solution. The pulp was then pumped through a pipe to a water extractor, and the spun-dry sanitized pulp was conveyed directly into a haul-away dumpster.

**In September Taylor reported there were 342 physicians already on the medical staff, with 58 applications pending.

***In those days there was strong patient loyalty, built up over time, to the generalists who were their family physicians. This bond of trust smoothed over the minor inconveniences at the hospital. Jean Dallas, whose husband, Carroll, was Director of Engineering at Lockheed, recounts: Grattan Woodson became their long-time family physician after one of her six children came to him with an allergic rash. Years later, when Robert, one of her sons in college, had an unusual problem, Chip referred him to urologist Nisbet Toole. Some detective work revealed a congenital abnormality of the blood vessels of one kidney. Emergency surgery was performed at the old St. Joseph's Infirmary downtown, because Northside's beds were filled. Robert was so impressed with Toole and his other doctors that he switched his college major from business administration to pre-med. He is now an anesthesiologist in Roanoke, Virginia.

During this period it was remarkable that no untoward incidents in patient care occurred. Some of the doctors felt they had been let down by an overall amateurish administrative management, "the gang who couldn't shoot straight." For them, the straw that broke the camel's back was yet another innovation, the infamous Service Control Center.

"The SCC," as it was referred to, was supposed to keep track, in one place, of ALL physician orders, wherever and whenever they originated in the hospital. In theory, at any given moment, by checking with the SCC, one could keep track of every patient's movements in terms of the patient's ordered schedule for the day. It could potentially give a bird's-eye view as well as comprehensive information of activity

Northside Hospital Celebrates Birthday

Miss Rita Englehart, director of patient care at Northside Hospital, and Hospital Administrator Joe Taylor share the honors in cutting a birthday cake celebrating the hospital's first anniversary. More than 600 employees attended the anniversary party on July 6 and were treated to punch, sandwiches, fruit, and cake.

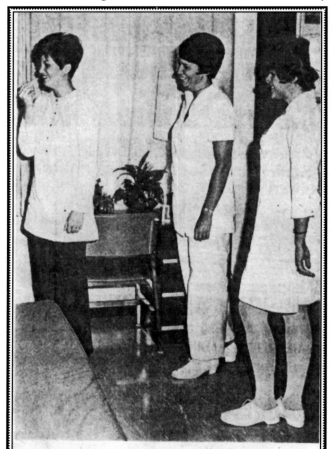

Staff Photo—Charles Pugh

LOOK CHANGES QUIETLY—As the mini-midi fashion controversy rages on, some nurses and other employes of metropolitan Atlanta hospitals are quietly taking on a new look. Pants-type uniforms now are optional attire at some area hospitals, while all women personnel at Cherokee Atomedic Hospital in Woodstock have switched to the pants uniforms. Northside Hospital employes shown in both the old and the new as they get ready for work are (from left) Judi Bowen, Teresa Marshall and Mrs. Margaret Broome.

From Atlanta Journal, Sept. 14, 1970

within the hospital on a given day, and provide information for billing. The concept may have been intriguing, but the details of how it was to work were a recipe for chaos.

First, a handwritten copy of any and all orders that the physician wrote would have to go directly and first to the SCC, which would then forward it to its destination, keeping track of it. This meant, for example, if the doctor ordered an emergency X-ray on his patient, the request did not come directly to Radiology, but would first have to go to the SCC. The handwritten copy of the doctor's orders, incidentally, was made by one of the high school graduates with little or no familiarity with medical matters, including terminology.

Second, at that time orders and other written communications within the hospital were sent via a pneumatic tube system. (The only computer system in the hospital was in the business office.) One had to put the felt end in first; if the other end went first, the tube could jam. One night a nurse sent her roommate some hand cream via the tube system. She put the tube in backwards, pulling the cream out of the tube, creating a mess and a really greasy tube system.

Samples of our experience in the Radiology Department give an idea of the problems encountered with the SCC elsewhere in the hospital: requests for emergency X-ray examinations would sometimes arrive a day or two later, or never, lost in the tube system. (And, of course, the referring physician was not aware we had not received his order.) It would have been infinitely easier, particularly in case of emergencies, to call us directly, which many physicians quickly learned to do.

Sometimes the handwritten copies of the doctors' orders were indecipherable or badly misspelled, and it was difficult to figure out the examination requested. To make matters worse, whoever designed the system liked the idea of substituting numbers for the names of the referring physicians, so sometimes we received a request for an examination we couldn't decipher, and we couldn't tell who the physician was because the assigned number did not match with the physician's name. The physician and nurse grapevine bypassed the system, and the catastrophes we feared might happen never materialized.

The SCC was canned fast.

▂▂▂▂

As Rufus Kervin put it, "Reality shock set in — for the founders, administration and staff — about five to seven months after the hospital opened. The one good thing was the unlimited demand for services; the hospital was filled to capacity." Both the administration and management staff began reevaluating themselves and their employees. Some employees were not of the caliber the founders had in mind. Some were discouraged by the modest and inconsistent paychecks. Some were simply wearing out. A number of employees were terminated or resigned at the end of 1970; this was stressful because some of those let go had been key figures. But, true to the cliche "It is always darkest before the dawn," during 1971 the hospital stabilized and kept improving.

▂▂▂▂

Two of the many other memorable aspects of the first year related to Vietnam and to mental health:

During the first two years several medical corpsmen who had served in Vietnam were part of the ER staff. They were technically good and considered themselves "junior doctors" (some subsequently went to medical school). But they created problems. Well-trained and tested in the field, they had become accustomed to making some medical decisions on their own. This may have been fitting and sometimes absolutely necessary under conditions in Vietnam, but not in a private practice hospital setting in Atlanta. The physicians decided the ER would function better without their help.

In the Vietnam era, which began (for the U.S.) two years before Northside opened,* a new type of clientele began showing up in increasing frequency in the emergency rooms of not only urban but suburban hospitals — heroin addicts and other severe drug abusers. Northside was very much aware of this and in its pre-opening plans gave concerted attention to security precautions.

In October 1970 plans for a Drug Crisis Center in operation around the clock were announced in a seminal conference on drug abuse at Northside's Community Mental Health Center. Charles Edwards, appointed full-time director of the Center** in September, inaugurated a full program to reduce drug abuse problems in the area and established the Suicide Prevention Center.

Edwards also tried to provide stress relief for Northside's middle management and others during the trying first six to nine months, and Kervin recalls

---

*The mythically tragic year of 1968, filled with searing images, shaped a generation: In January, during the Vietnamese New Year's celebration of Tet, the North Vietnamese launched a pounding offensive against U.S.-held bases and Communists swarmed into the U.S. Embassy. In March, President Lyndon B. Johnson announced he would not seek second term. In April, Dr. Martin Luther King, Jr., was assassinated. More than 100 cities erupted in violence. In June, Robert Kennedy was gunned down. During the Democratic Convention in Chicago that summer, war erupted between protesters and police. In August, Soviet tanks rolled into Czechoslovakia. In November, Richard M. Nixon defeated Hubert Humphrey for the presidency. The unemployment rate was 3.5%, the lowest since 1953. It was the year Bill Clinton graduated from college.

**This operated as a strictly private self-sustaining institution, and the center had no connection with the hospital other than a sharing of facilities for convenience. It was financed with 50% federal funds matched by local private funds.

being invited to Edwards' "T" groups (in this case, not "tea," as in crumpets, but "T," as in therapy). These Friday mid-morning roundtable sessions were multi-flavored: "part cheering section, part ventilation and expression of feelings, including the empowerment to disagree, and part sounding board for consensus and future directions," appropriate and useful at the time.

▼▼▼▼

There were no physiotherapy facilities initially, but these came in six months, following groundwork by Bill Collins and his committee of busy orthopedists, and Physical Therapy would become a department in 1971.

▼▼▼▼

When Emmy-lou Faber agreed to become the education director, one of her chief complaints was that there was no medical library. She was told, "Well, open one." How much money was available? "Oh, there's no money; we can't even meet the payroll." She quickly learned that the many things which had to be done would have to be done on a shoestring, at best. She went to Bill Huger,* head of the medical staff's Education and Research Committee, and told him she was applying for a grant from the National Library of Medicine. The committee was amused by the zeal of this nurse educator, but Huger promised her that if she secured the grant the doctors would match it somehow. She did receive the grant, a little over $3,000, and Huger and his committee got the medical staff to contribute $4,000 (draining off more than half of the staff's treasury, which it had accumulated from dues).

For professional help, Faber went to the Dean of Emory's Library School, who offered her the guidance of a professor who was teaching courses in graduate school. Northside's library became the graduate students' project, they became her official consultants, and the library opened in the spring of 1971.**

▼▼▼▼

It was typical of the executive committee of the medical staff that in January 1971, little more than six months after Northside opened, it had already appointed a Rate Review Committee, chaired by David Cohen, to evaluate the cost of medical care at Northside in relation to other hospitals, with the purpose of keeping costs down. Specific areas included ER, Laboratory, Pharmacy, Radiology, Semiprivate and Private Rooms. A final analysis was reported in December.

▼▼▼▼

Transition and changes in nurses' uniforms and employee dress codes were a characteristic of that time. The distinctive nurse's cap and starched white dress began disappearing. Attention was called to the problem of "see through blouses," and the importance of "proper underwear." (A few employees had not bothered to wear any.) Northside's personal appearance code was too liberal for some, and one surgical patient from central Georgia became upset at the heavily bearded visage of the orderly who bent over him, the last thing he remembered before he was wheeled to major surgery.

▼▼▼▼

By spring of the first year, things fell into place and Northside began becoming what everyone originally had in mind.

---

*Huger, a plastic surgeon, was a warm and friendly bear, and another of the physicians whose medical loyalties were primarily elsewhere (Piedmont Hospital, in his case), but who did yeoman service in behalf of Northside. He had been active on the Building Committee and vice-president of the medical staff.

**Some of the first medical books in the library were selected from those donated by doctors' widows. Faber had no money available for physical help, but she talked the Scoutmaster in charge of her son's troop into having the Boy Scouts volunteer to unpack boxes of books and set up the shelves. Initially the students from Emory helped man the library, and the Pink Ladies pitched in (some had been librarians in their earlier days). From such humble beginnings the medical library, which was then located centrally in the hospital, got off to a good start.

15

After the Deluge

By the time of the first anniversary in July 1971, Taylor was breathing easier. Outpatient surgery had begun in April, and the use of OB facilities was so great that new physicians were being discouraged from joining the staff. The obstetricians who also practiced at Georgia Baptist asked Northside's anesthesiology group if they were interested in administering epidural anesthesia at Baptist so that they could send their patients there instead of Northside, because the latter's service was too busy for the present facilities.

Despite its financial problems, the hospital was fast acquiring a deserved reputation for fine patient care. Demand was far in excess of beds, necessitating the early discharge of patients. Priorities in expansion planning were ER facilities and, of course, OB. Physicians in other specialties in medicine and surgery were becoming concerned that the needs of their own sections which had not yet been met would have to wait even longer because of the very success of OB and the ER. Yet more doctors kept coming, totalling over 400. The number of hospital employees had increased to 550.

Patients were still having difficulty finding the hospital. The Fulton County Public Works Department had promised but had still not put up signs along the county's roads leading to the hospital.

The trio of pathology, radiology and anesthesiology (the latter particularly in obstetrics) became a popular attraction of the hospital because they focused on service more than did other Atlanta hospitals at that time. (This was in addition to their reliable, up-to-date professional skills and technology.) For example, most laboratories in Atlanta quit after 4 p.m., did no work except emergencies until 7 a.m. the following day and performed no routine work on weekends. Under Ray Graves, Northside's lab in 1971 began to "do anything anyone wanted — anytime."

A five-story, 90,000-square-foot medical building, designed to accommodate offices of almost 100 doctors, was completed next door, on four acres leased from the Hospital Authority. The authority had decided to let a private developer own and operate the building instead of committing public funds, and to choose its real estate agent from among a group of selected bidders. Northside Realty Associates, winner of the bid, brought in the Landmarks Group (which built the nearby Executive Suites and the Concourse complex) as owner-developer-manager.

The word came that an applied-for inspection by the Joint Commission on Accreditation of Hospitals would take place near the end of 1971, creating both anxiety and enthusiasm. This official stamp of approval, which was a matter of pride to the hospital and reassurance for the public, was an eligibility requirement for reimbursement from Medicare/Medicaid, which accounted for about 18% of the hospital's billings at that time. Northside easily passed, but not without the yeoman work of Dr. David Cohen and a newly arrived COO.

"We were extremely innovative while the inspection team was there," Emmy-lou Faber recalls. For example, the entire east wing of the sixth floor was a pediatric unit, which contained some cribs. At times, space was needed for adults, and it was necessary to swing the cribs out and temporarily put in regular-size beds for adults. (Early on, the hospital had to rent these adult beds since it did not have enough. When it could afford to buy them, it kept the extra adult beds stored in the back hall, on the other side of the elevator.) Unfortunately, the JCAH inspection team could flunk you if it found beds or equipment stored in the halls. The solution: the staff ran the extra beds up and down on the elevator, out of the path of the inspection team.

Taylor needed more administrative help, and the authority agreed. In preparation for the inspection by the Joint Commission and to replace his assistant, George Lansdell, who had left at the beginning of the year, he called Hospital Association executives around the Southeast for recommendations. The best one came from the president of the North Carolina Association; he suggested Chris Clark.

Brought up in a generational family of doctors, Clark changed his major from Pre-Med to Business Administration when he was a junior at Vanderbilt. He earned a Master's degree in the latter at the University of Chicago, majoring in Health Administration, and was assigned to the Baptist Hospital in Winston Salem for his administrative residency. There he had worked almost 8 years,* when Taylor called.

The job was offered and accepted quickly, and Clark came to work at Northside on September 1, 1971, as Associate Administrator-Operations, today's equivalent of a Chief Operations Officer (COO).

While Clark was being interviewed and considered for the job, Taylor told him how he (Taylor) originally had been a planning consultant for the board and had evolved into being the administrator. He was still working on his Ph.D. at Georgia State when he was able to squeeze in the time; he did not know how long it would take (it turned out to be 13 years), but as he had also told the board, he still eventually wanted to be a teacher. He had enjoyed being a planner, and in fact, enjoyed line management. Clark said, "He enjoyed everything he did — a very turned-on, happy person." He said, according to Clark, "It won't be too long before I'm gone; if you come and you are successful, you'll have a good opportunity for promotion into my job." Clark found him a "very attractive man to work with."

Rufus Kervin's first impressions of Clark were: "When he came here, he had 'operations' written all over him. As he came into the organization, he began to put a lot of structure into place. I recall meetings with him working on budgets and tables of organizations; one thing that characterized him was that these had to be accurate down to the decimal point. I recall sessions with him which were very regimented, even to the point of making sure that there were no erasures, no typing strikeovers, every dot dotted, every 'T' crossed. This was a real contrast with Joe Taylor and his era — when we got together and had meetings we talked about feelings and thoughts and how to approach things. Clark was clearly a shift in the organization and the operation when he arrived."

Clark had his own first impressions of Northside: "I remember how impressed I was with how the physicians and the members of the board were in concert on what they were looking for and where they wanted to go, and that they were working together with Joe to staff this position, in sort of a team effort. That's why I came. But when I came, I am sure that I was quite naive and did not ask very many hard questions, and really had very little notion at all what I was getting myself into.

"My greatest memory of the hospital at that time was facing the Joint Commission, staring us in the face in almost no time at all; there was a great deal to do to prepare for that. Second, the hospital was totally full, all the time. The hospital's cash position was still poor** and we still did not have a lot of basic tools, like good computer services."

How did Northside meet those challenges? Clark's summary of that time echoes Taylor: "Northside had an extraordinary group of people who worked tirelessly and who worked smart, and made do with little to make it best for the patient and for the doctor. But we all knew that we were not able to guarantee that the feast of high utilization would last, and that famine would come if we did not get things straightened out."

One of the first sighs of relief came with a mini-expansion completed in August 1972, which tripled the size of the emergency area and expanded maternity services.

---

*It was a most unusual organization. Baptist Hospital and the Bowman Gray School of Medicine were separate corporate entities occupying the same block (and with the same common training programs), but with no common governance, much less common executive ranks. The two organizations barely communicated. Clark says he became the first bridge person between the two institutions, resulting from their need to plan together for expansion.

As a resident, Clark asked for the job of taking on the planning of what turned out to be an almost 80 million dollar complex of 8 to 10 buildings over the next 8 years. He was given responsibility for Nursing, Diagnostic and Treatment Services, for the house staff, coordination of chiefs of professional services and for all services shared between the medical school and the hospital (the computer system, power plants, etc.).

**The hospital's financial position was not helped by President Nixon's general wage and price freeze in August, 1971. These controls were not lifted on health care until April, 1974. (Incidentally, in 1972 medical prices edged up only 3.3%, but after the controls were lifted they skyrocketed to 12.4% in 1974.)

16

New Neighbors

Other hospitals and planners of would-be hospitals in the Atlanta area were watching Northside's rise and development with great interest. They were impressed by the seemingly unlimited demand for hospital beds, the high quality of patient care (as well as by the immediate, spectacular popularity of the state-of-the-art obstetrical service, specifically), by the exceptional medical staff, by those innovative features of the hospital that worked well, and by the demographic characteristics of the area.

And not least, they were intrigued by the geographic accessibility of this "suburban" hospital in relation to the future growth of Atlanta.

For example, the 48-bed Scottish Rite Hospital for Crippled Children,* in the East Lake portion of Decatur, in need of a new and larger facility and aware of its increasingly inaccessible location, confronted an estimate by its consultant that "by 1990 the center of the population density of Atlanta would be at the intersection of I-285 and GA 400."

By 1971, Northside's pediatricians had already come to the conclusion that the hospital, with its extensive commitments but quite limited funds, was not going to have the strong pediatric service which would meet their patients' needs and their own. They knew well Northside's dreams and hopes and goals, because they had been an integral part of the hospital from the beginning and had helped shape them and fight for them.** They knew firsthand of Northside's needs because they were directly responsible for taking care of the mounting swarm of babies in facilities which were already inadequate.

They also knew that Northside, as a self-declared independent, non-profit community hospital, had turned its back on the usual sources of large financial support (proprietary hospital chain or sponsorship by a church or other single private organization).*** Big bucks would be needed to transform Northside's promises into reality, but, it became increasingly clear, the main source of "surplus funds" would have to be the slow and steady, but relatively modest, distillate from charges for services provided to patients. Taylor said, "I knew Jud was disappointed that we really didn't go into a full-fledged pediatric service, but he was too much of a gentleman to say much about it."

In 1971, Hawk and his good friend Wood Lovell, the widely respected orthopedist who was the mainstay of Scottish Rite and its teaching program (following in the footsteps of the legendary Dr. Hiram Kite),

---

*The first hospital in Georgia to be devoted totally to children, it focused on orthopedic problems. It was the first full-charity "crippled children's" hospital in the country and, possibly, in the world.

**Ralph Robinson and Jerry Berman were the earliest pediatricians in the area (aside from Leila Denmark, who was never associated with Northside). Jud Hawk was the first chairman of the formal medical staff in 1968. Mike Levine was a forceful, active participant before and after the hospital opened. Scott James was also active as chairman of the medical staff in 1975-1976.

***Although sponsorship by a Hospital Authority had its advantages, the latter could not participate in joint commercial ventures and could not take advantage of the venture capital which was becoming increasingly available. Also, the terms under which Northside's Hospital Authority sponsorship was approved precluded access to tax-based public funds. And finally, there were no potential wealthy private benefactors on the horizon (and the fund-raising Northside Foundation did not come into being until 1985. The auxiliary did what it could, securing $1,850,000 in gifts and pledges over a 20-year period, but this was only a drop in the bucket in comparison to the needs).

came to talk with Taylor about the possibility of Scottish Rite building a complete children's facility across the street from the main entrance to Northside.

That suited Taylor just fine. After all, it would free up some badly needed beds at Northside, which was constantly filled to capacity. It would also cut down on the extent of Northside's commitments, give the pediatricians what they wanted, and would be in the best interest of patient care. Scottish Rite and the associated physicians and laymen were all highly regarded, and Taylor knew and respected Tommy Reddin, the administrator. And it would be a big asset to the Northside medical complex and its growth. To him and to the authority, it appeared to be a win-win situation, and they gave it their blessing.*

Less than a year later, in 1972, Rawson Haverty,** chairman of the board of St. Joseph's Infirmary, called the chairman of Northside's authority to set up a meeting with those two and Taylor. The meeting, Haverty said, was to talk about a report that a consultant had given to his hospital regarding the possibility of St. Joseph's buying some property across the street and relocating there.

The plight of venerable St. Joseph's, Atlanta's oldest hospital, run by the Catholic Sisters of Mercy, was well known. Founded in 1880 in a small house on Baker Street, it moved to a 10-bed facility on Courtland Street (now the site of the Marriott Marquis). It expanded to about 150 beds in the early 1900s and doubled with an Ivy Street wing in 1953. Badly needed, extensive renovations at the cramped Ivy Street location had been discussed for five years. Renovations of the Courtland Street wing would cost $8 to $10 million, and half of the beds dated back to the early 1900s. Parking was an ongoing problem. Atlanta was growing away from St. Joseph's, and its patient population was changing. According to an article in the *Atlanta Constitution* (Nov. 25, 1972), "Catholic occupancy for the past several years was running about 10% of the total hospital patient population; the percentage of black patients was growing (from 9% in 1967 to 14% in 1971)." Weighing everything, they decided to move. And so they talked about how the area around Northside could be the right place.

In hindsight, Taylor says Haverty's meeting with them was partly diplomatic courtesy and partly to determine whether the authority would officially object to St. Joseph's coming, since St. Joseph's already had an option on 20 acres, which it promptly exercised. "Rawson was a pretty persuasive guy," Taylor said, "and he convinced us there was enough demand in the area to support another hospital." Taylor and the authority did not object, and so told Haverty. It was clear that St. Joseph's had already decided to come.

The administrative staff of both hospitals (Sister Mary Brian Anderson was St. Joseph's Administrator; Charles Burge, her Associate Administrator), met several times to work out "shared arrangements" and other details. According to Taylor, both hospitals were going to share security systems, computer systems, yards and grounds services, and would swap information on bad debts — "everything except clinical services." Both hospitals would "share administrative expenses in any way possible" and pledged their mutual cooperation and support.

The medical staff would remain two independent and unique organizations, and conduct their own affairs and make their own decisions.

In February 1973, Bob van de Wetering, the chairman of Northside's Medical Staff, announced that a Northside physicians' committee (Lea Richmond, David Cohen and John McCoy as floating substitute), acting as liaison between the medical staffs of St. Joseph's and Northside, had also made a great deal of progress, and mentioned functions which could be shared. (Many months later van de Wetering and Richmond agreed to meet with Rhodes Haverty in a Commerce Club meeting set up by attorney Ben Kohler, a supporter of St. Joseph's. Kohler introduced them and then left. The meeting was for the purpose of giving Haverty whatever advice he would solicit in relation to St. Joseph's move. They found him impressive, although Bob was surprised that Haverty was "a bit condescending.")

Taylor also began having meetings with Tommy Reddin, Scottish Rite's administrator, since the idea of shared services and shared expenses was appeal-

---

*Wilbur Fisk Glenn contributed the money to purchase the original eight acres of land across from Northside at $40,000 per acre. The campus now embraces 18-1/2 acres. The 1993 asking price of a contiguous three acres was $750,000 per acre, according to Hawk.
**His brother, Rhodes Haverty, was at that time a pediatrician on Northside's medical staff; subsequently Rhodes left to become Director of Allied Health Sciences at Georgia State University.

ing. If one could make it work, it could also be a win-win situation for all three hospitals: decrease costs (to each hospital) while improving the efficiency of services. All three hospitals were indeed interested, and the news article in the *Atlanta Constitution* in November 1972, announcing St. Joseph's Infirmary's plans to move from downtown and form a medical care triangle with Northside and Scottish Rite, stated, "The three-hospital plan suggests cost-sharing in such areas as computer services, laundry services and group purchasing."

"To avoid duplicating services at the proposed three-hospital medical complex, St. Joseph's would specialize in neurological, vascular and coronary care and would have complete facilities for open heart surgery. It would not provide obstetrical services now offered at Northside, and will not offer pediatric care that will be provided by Scottish Rite Hospital." Nothing was mentioned in the article about the emergency room; Taylor and Clark said they were told by St. Joseph's that the latter had no plans for an ER, since Northside's Emergency area was just across the street. Northside also had a mental health section which St. Joseph's had no intention of duplicating.

Taylor recalled a very cordial and cooperative relationship between himself and Charles Burge, the associate administrator at St. Joseph's (and also with the chief operating officer there) and with Tommy Reddin of Scottish Rite and his staff. "We talked about and planned all kinds of shared services." Both hospitals were under construction when he left Northside in September 1973 to go to Georgia State.

In 1972 and 1973 another kind of feeling arose, Taylor said, which was epitomized in Chris Clark, his assistant administrator and COO, who was very much opposed to working in cooperation with St. Joseph's or Scottish Rite, because he considered them competition. The decision had already been made for both these hospitals to build next to Northside before he

came, and they had already been extended a welcoming hand, but he expressed that opposition — at first softly and then more outspokenly: Northside should not be working with the competition. The medical staff did not have that attitude, although a few of the doctors and board members did resent the fact that after all the years of groundwork it took to get Northside built and running, another hospital (which was having a difficult time elsewhere) had plopped itself alongside, in position to reap the benefits of Northside's pioneering efforts without having to endure any of the pain. But Taylor himself was troubled by Clark's reaction.

Clark now smiles wryly, as he recalls that period. "Yes, it's true; I did feel strongly they were competition. But you must remember, I came to Northside from a tertiary care center in a highly competitive area where we had been having to fight for economic survival. At Northside, Joe ran a hospital where all the beds were filled and there was no competition. I had a hard time convincing him how quickly the winds of change would be coming," but as Northside's chief operating officer, he felt his responsibility was to tell Taylor the unvarnished reality.

Although Clark arrived in September 1971, he was never involved in the discussions on shared services* and was not asked for his input. The only thing he knew about was the emergency room. The ER had proved to be an important, even vital, source of patient admissions at Northside, and Clark wanted to make sure that St. Joseph's did not have one. After all, St. Joseph's had not found it necessary to have an ER downtown, and had not applied for one in the Certificate of Need (CON) application which was required at that time of hospitals planning new services, so they would not duplicate existing facilities. According to Clark, St. Joseph's later quietly added one in the plan, which he spotted and with which he confronted Sister Mary Brian, the Administrator. He

---

*According to Clark, whatever the reason, after St. Joseph's opened, Northside was actually never able to get its new neighbor to do anything about the shared services it had agreed upon earlier. Northside and its departmental managers put forward many presentations and proposals but they seemed to evaporate somewhere along the approval pathway.

During Clark's tenure (1973-1988), he said St. Joseph's and Northside did agree to and did share:

(1) Cutting the grass on the median on Peachtree Dunwoody Road every other time.

(2) A typewriter maintenance contract (saving $5/month per contract).

(3) Years later, and after greatly protracted negotiation, an MRI (magnetic resonance) unit, on Northside property. This became a constant source of frustration.

Both Scottish Rite and St. Joseph's did join Northside's Employee Assistance Program and, for a time, used Northside's Home Health Service. Northside offered to join in a common child care center, no matter where it was located, but each decided to build its own.

says she never forgave him for that. Sister Mary Brian, with a somewhat wily touch, was even more fiercely protective of her turf than Clark was of Northside.

〰〰〰

In the late '60s and early '70s, proprietary hospitals blossomed throughout the country as the result of liberal Medicare rules reimbursing hospitals for their costs (and allowing rapid depreciation), plus the expansion of private health insurance.

On October 22, 1972, the 178-bed Shallowford Community Hospital opened, three expressway exits away. This proprietary (for-profit) hospital in North DeKalb County was owned by Charter Medical Corporation based in Macon, Georgia. Walter Hood, an internist on Northside's staff, was president of the Shallowford Medical Staff. Shallowford had an ER. Almost every new hospital would have an ER.

Twelve days later, the proprietary (HCA) West Paces Ferry Hospital also opened, also adjacent an expressway, closer to downtown. And in 1973, closer to Marietta, the proprietary Urban Medical Hospital, started by Dr. Larry Cooper, a medical oncologist, opened on Windy Hill Road. (In 1980 it was purchased by Kennestone and renamed "Windy Hill Hospital.")

The era of competition was beginning.

2

Afterwards

What happened on The Hill in the twenty years since Joe Taylor left? Northside's life passed through two new chapters and into a third, a medical milieu and business/political environment far different from the early days. Each of these three phases has had its own distinct flavor and its own truths to be learned. At Northside, the first fifteen of these years was dominated by Christopher Clark.

By 1993, The Hill had become a major entity in Atlanta medical care.

17

The Era of the Cool Administrator (1973-1988)

When he came to Northside as its new chief operating officer under Joe Taylor in September 1971, 31-year-old Christopher Clark was the right man for the job. Well trained, nuts-and-bolts practical and supremely self-disciplined, he brought needed order and organization to the hospital operation.

His personal traits were sharply etched. For starters, he was very bright, highly analytical, with a passion for details and a remarkable memory. Ted Walker, who came to Northside as the head of Pharmacy in 1971, remembers, "Chris was an extremely orderly individual with almost never a hair out of place, and it would be unusual to see his coat unbuttoned when outside his office." At the same time, he was affable, polite and smiled readily. Articulate, he clearly expressed what he wanted to say, and was never at a loss for appropriate words when called upon.

He was scrupulously honest in matters pertaining to the hospital's finances. He was a good father and a devoted family man (his fine wife, Linda, is a nurse at Scottish Rite) and a devout Baptist, with no appreciable vices.

Clark had many virtues, and a little side business of selling Rolex watches and oriental rugs, which might seem inappropriate for a CEO, but this diversion just seemed to make him appear more human. He came by this talent honestly since his Baptist minister grandfather, with whom he spent a lot of time in his youth, had a penchant for trading.

But nobody is perfect. Clark's imperfection was an extraordinary, pervasive need for control, more than was necessary to do his job well. (It was said of

Christopher Clark

him, "He's the kind of guy who won't take yes for an answer.") This trait might have been useful, even laudable, when he was a COO, but being an administrator was a little different. In time, as the hospital expanded and became more complex, and local and national changes and challenges affecting the delivery of health care became less manageable, this attribute would create problems for him, for some of those he worked with, and for Northside.

In retrospect, he was a particularly interesting personality in that he was viewed so differently by different people, more so than any of the other three administrators in Northside's history. The author submits that three additional characteristics contributed to this sometime ambiguity: (1) Clark's genuine desire to please (when it did not cost him anything). He liked to tell you what you wanted to hear, even if it did not always turn out that way; (2) his non-aggressive persona; and (3) most of all, his obvious fondness and pride in Northside and his dedication to it. In recognition ceremonies he relished telling employees what a great hospital they were in and how Northside was filled with people who cared. And he meant every word. No one ever accused him of having an agenda other than Northside's. Chris was a great rationalizer; one did not question his dedication to what he believed was in Northside's best interest. He was usually right, especially in the earlier part of his 15-year-tenure, but what he felt was in the hospital's best interest was not always necessarily so.

David Cohen, a former chairman of both the medical staff and the Northside Foundation, summarized his management style: "An extremely steep pyramid. Everything that happened in the hospital cleared through him. He didn't delegate responsibility and, in the short fall, he had to monitor everything." One might not always agree with his conclusions, but one could be assured he would hardly ever make a move without careful planning and calculation.

<hr>

A Manager's-Eye View of the Clark Era

To capture the essence and highlights of that time in these few pages, there is no better way to begin than with the keen overview (echoed by others) of one of Chris's long-time managers, Rufus Kervin, director of the laboratory:

He quickly brought in a number of new "young lieutenants," and the bureaucracy expanded — horizontally and vertically — and became cumbersome. In the larger organization, who reported to whom became a big consideration, and new job descriptions had to be developed. He was famous for his emphasis on organization and hierarchy structuring to accomplish our mission. Some of the people around him seemed like buffers; in the corporate structure some were afraid to talk back. The growth in support func-

tions clearly outpaced growth in other areas. There were entire new functions and new bureaucracies.

There was focus on these new functions, and the people heading them had high tech skills and were graduates of MHA and MBA programs, but the majority had no hands-on experience in patient care. This meant a change in direction; the burden of the quality of care shifted to middle management.

We had had strong, efficient, capable department heads with experience in managing people, focusing on patients and physicians and their needs. We had grown up in a different, hands-on era, rising through the ranks. Most of our peers were similar in these respects. Now there was another layer of people between us and administration who did not have this focus. This was significant.

The "young lieutenants" wanted to use their basketful of skills. They wanted to be competitive in building buildings and starting new programs. They began consuming large resources, dictated from the strategic plan standpoint, to put Northside in the best competitive position in Certificate of Need (CON) battles, enlarging services and defending markets.

About 1975, I saw some of these trends, saw who the people were who were elevated to levels of decision-making, and decided to become professionally trained in the area of management. I went back and got an MBA degree. Now I had the advantages of both worlds — both street smarts and the corporate, accounting view of the "young lieutenants" — and I could appreciate both focuses Northside was taking.

The era of competition started after Scottish Rite and St. Joseph's opened in the latter half of the seventies. The hospital was willing — and financially able — to spend more on technology than it was ever willing to do before. In that period I began to realize that technology can give you a competitive advantage for only a short time, if any, and that, in the long range, the area of service was most important. We had to relearn that principle, and we keep having to relearn that, even at present.

One of the new technologies had a major impact. It was a major consumer of resources and a major element in the structure, organization and delivery of care — computerization.* We got our own first computer in 1975. In the lab, with our automated answering service, and automation in requesting and charging for ancillary services, we (*he said, with a smile*) could do wrong things faster.

In 1975-76, Northside began to lose its original goal, quality patient care. I believe it was because of the hierarchy and the support areas which did not see a link and relationship of their specific job to patients and physicians.

---

*Clark believes one of his best decisions was the extensive computerization system of HBO, which worked well at the lowest cost and was used as a model for other hospitals.

We moved away from core business, taking care of patients and physicians.

By 1984, the trend and the gap was recognized by many. There were cracks there, and people wondered how to correct them. Between 1984 and 1987, the dust, trauma and noise of Northside's lengthy, major renovation in most departments had taken a toll on morale and spirit, and clouded the horizon on where Northside was going as an institution. It caused more movement away from seeing Northside through physicians' and patients' eyes and needs.

It was the end of an era, the end of a relationship. The last two years, Chris's work became much more political. He was not willing to rely on lots of give and take and commonality of assumptions. For some reason, he failed to invest sufficiently in relationships, and we did not maintain a relationship sufficient to continue on the journey to our original goal.

⋀⋀⋀⋀

The Seventies

Clark came to Northside chanting the mantra of cost-containment and cost-effectiveness, and not without reason. In 1973, the year he became administrator, an important line was crossed in this country. For the first time, health care became more expensive than national defense, rising to 11.3% of the national budget from 4.4% in 1965. (In 1992, it rose to nearly three times the defense budget — 13.4% of the gross domestic product.) In the first half of the '70s, there were national outcries of a financial "crisis" in health care, abetted by a weak economy and inflation.

Clark was a man of his times. With the aid of board members like Gulf Oil's Jack Marquis,* he initiated Northside into the business-like approach to running hospitals. It was needed, but the innocence of the early days was lost forever.

By the time Taylor left in 1973, Clark was firmly in control. Hospital utilization was high, and the business operation improved. He announced the construction of a four-story, $9-million-annex which added 98 beds (a total of 348) and two operating suites, doubling the size of the coronary care unit and expanding the intensive care unit. The project was to be completed in two years.

He was proud of his capital allocation (budgeting) system. Things requested by physicians and that served patients were in a category separate from non-medical equipment or garden variety medical tools. Each year he had each department of the medical staff prioritize the list of items which they requested (along with price and documentation of need). The management team did the same with non-medical items. As the authority allotted funds, it was a simple matter to pick from the prioritized list. He liked it because it "basically avoided fights and confrontation." That was easy for him to say, because he left it up to the departments of the medical staff to reason and negotiate with each other.

The process worked well and it avoided the problems in some other hospitals where the squeakiest or most powerful wheel got the most attention. Clark's own input to the authority may have influenced the total amount the authority was willing and able to allocate, but he was predictably parsimonious. "We wasted almost nothing."

At that time there was a nursing shortage locally and nationally, and he sent Jean Giblin, the chief of nurses, and Emmy-lou Faber to the Philippines to recruit nurses for one to two year contracts. Georgia Baptist Hospital also recruited there at that time.

In April 1974, 20 Filipino registered nurses, some with bachelor's degrees, joined Northside. Overall, it did not work out well. There were language (dialect) and custom barriers to communication, especially over the telephone, and many of the nurses were homesick. This episode faded away as a dip in the economy brought more American nurses, who had been busy raising families, back into the workplace.

1974 was a typical busy year at Northside.** There was once more a severe problem in maternity

---

*Marquis, Gulf's chief financial officer for the Southeast, was a good friend of County Commissioner Milton Farris, who had also been at Gulf. At the time Clark came to Northside, Farris had been worrying about the new hospital's financial picture. The hospital owed everyone and got delivery of goods, drugs and equipment only with cash in advance. Farris nominated Marquis, who joined the board in April 1971, shortly after Chris came. Clark found Marquis to be "a wonderful board member, financially astute, with good judgment." Marquis was a Northside neighbor, living on nearby Kingston Road. Early on he had been actively opposed to the hospital's site location, but he turned into a staunch friend and supporter.

**The dialysis center opened; the first guidelines for saline abortion were adopted; the uro-dynamics service was approved; and pharmacy acquired a computer system. Nurse Shirley Davis was appointed in charge of the new service Patient Concerns. (The following December, another outstanding nurse, Marilyn Gillespie, came to Northside as the new head of patient care and contributed to further upgrading the nursing service.) Radiology received its first, "state of the art" mammography unit. Earl Hathcock, the obstetrician who had been chairman of the medical staff, and then moved to the board, was the first physician to die in office.

THE PASSAGE OF SHIRLEY DAVIS, RN

Among the very fine nurses during Northside's history, Mrs. Howard Davis was another example of how someone who loved her work awakened to her own managerial abilities and became progressively involved in new challenges and new solutions.

Before the hospital opened, she often drove by as the building went up and decided that this was where she wanted to work. Her first application was turned down (someone said it was because Northside at that time could afford to hire only a limited number of registered nurses and the personnel office seemed to give preference to ladies with pretty legs). In August 1970 the hospital decided it needed another I.V. Nurse (to give intravenous medications) in pharmacy and she began in that capacity. At that time Atlanta hospitals generally did not allow nurses to do I.V.'s, the task being performed by doctors. Davis and Lynn Bell, whom she said was the first I.V. nurse, together drew up policies and procedures, which were approved by the medical staff, and they operated as a team. Emory, Georgia Baptist, DeKalb and Kennestone sent their personnel to Northside to observe before setting up their own I.V. teams.

As a Medical-Surgical Nurse, her potential was noticed. In 1972 she was asked to become the nurse in charge of Infection Control and she reported to the medical committee. In addition, she was asked to serve in Utilization Review (UR), in which she studied a sampling of the patients' hospital charts, the 16th day of the patient's hospitalization. This turned out to be instructive. One patient, for example, could have been discharged but was still in the hospital because his house had burned down, and the family had not yet been able to make the necessary arrangements. This and other incidents showed the need for routine discharge planning, which she recommended.

This became one of the several varied functions of a new department which she was asked by Chris Clark to head in 1974. This unique department, which she named Patient Concerns, acted as an ombudsman for patients, families and the hos-

pital community. It answered any question that was not medical. It was located around the corner from the emergency department and came to be relied upon so much that in 1977 she was allowed to start a very useful Patient Representative program. The rep maintained communication between the patient in the treatment area and his (her) family or friends in the waiting area, provided information to the patient while he/she was waiting to be seen by the staff and directed the patient to other parts of the hospital as necessary. The rep also provided the ER with feedback regarding patient problems or dissatisfactions, etc. In addition to the ER, the reps were also in the surgery, outpatient admissions and "on rounds" areas.

Initially, Davis's Patient Concerns was a department of one. Within four years she had five employees. She was greatly encouraged by administration, particularly George Simpson, the assistant administrator, and by middle managers under Simpson — June Morrison, Leonard Ridings and Rufus Kervin. At home she was also a busy wife and mother with five children.

Responding to problems uncovered by discharge planning, she and her Patient Concerns department began the first hospital-based Home Health Service in Georgia in 1978. This was an immediately popular alternative to avoid the high costs and confinement of a hospital. Northside's patients felt more comfortable with this continuity of service, which was also able to provide critical care nursing and I.V. therapy. Also, with the large OB section, there were a certain number of patients (who threatened early abortion, etc.) who needed daily monitoring at home by a nurse before delivery. Her group also started the Apnea Monitoring program (1979) and, finally, the Hospice program, as part of Home Health Services. She remained in charge of Patient Concerns for nine years, until 1983.

Shirley Davis retired five years ago, grateful that she was involved in a place that allowed her to do the things she thought challenging, and happy that she did them all well.

bed space, and on four occasions Labor & Delivery was closed to all admissions, and new physician applications to the obstetrical staff were put on hold for a year. But in 1974-75 there was a severe economic recession and soaring inflation, and in August 1975 Clark reported to the medical staff, "The hospital has not yet experienced the full occupancy of new beds as expected. Physicians are urged to let patients know that there is no longer a waiting list and to make every effort to fill these beds as quickly as possible."

In 1974 a new health planning law was passed and all states were required to pass certificate-of-need (CON) legislation and to establish State Health Planning and Development agencies (SHPDA's). (CON requirements are still in effect.)

Also in 1974, Clark was to experience the first of what he considers his three biggest disappointments or frustrations at Northside. Hit by the recession, the Landmarks group was trying to liquidate the last 10 acres of land contiguous to Northside,* extending next to the expressway. Landmarks' head, Blaine Kelly, offered it to Northside first, and Clark was excited. "Will you take $100,000?" he asked. Kelly said the price was more like $1 million. Clark realized that even at that stiff price, it was worth it, but he could not convince the board. It was bad timing; Northside had finally gotten out of debt and had consolidated its cash position but it had only a couple of million dollars in the bank and the board felt it could be criticized for "wasting patients' and taxpayers' money on something we don't need and will never need." Clark felt it was an opportunity which would never come again, but the Board still said no.

▃▃▃

Clark ran a tight ship; the hospital had relatively steady, calculated growth from late 1975 through the next nine years. It was the calmest period in Northside's history, and some physicians considered that during this span it reached its zenith. The first major expansion was completed in 1975, and in 1977 Radiation Therapy (designated a separate department in 1979), CT (Computerized Tomography) equipment and other facilities were

added. St. Joseph's opened in 1976 and Scottish Rite in 1978, but Northside was king of The Hill, and its trajectory was still upward.**

Some equipment and services were not obtained as quickly as physicians felt they needed, but with the big, diverse medical staff and limited budget this was to be expected. Overall, they fared well compared to other local hospitals, since Clark was committed to grow quickly towards tertiary service.

▃▃▃

Psychiatrist Tom Gable recalls that part of the excitement when he came to practice at Northside in the early '70s was that, "Basically, the physicians really ran the hospital." He did not mean that literally; what he referred to was the friendly collegiality between the administrator, the medical staff and the board. When the medical staff spoke, Joe Taylor listened; when their requests were reasonable and they did not cost money (policies, for example), he gave them what they asked for.

The physician founders had always championed the principle of equality among medical staff members; spreading the leadership and other obligations around enabled them to resume their full-time attention to the practice of medicine. They were well aware that the purposeful democratization and diffusion of leadership responsibility in this big medical staff, with a change of officers every year, could itself create risks and problems for the physicians. But they believed that approach was better than the alternatives.

Their primary concern being the quality of patient care, it had always been assumed that whatever was best for the patient coincided with what was best for Northside and for its physicians. As the reality of financial restrictions, the awareness of imperfections inherent in the operation of a complex, growing hospital, and Chris Clark's management style all came into sharper focus, certain conclusions became starkly evident. Hard choices were going to have to be made — and often. Physicians could no longer leave it up to the hospital to determine what constituted optimum patient care or what was in the best interest of the doctors' professional needs. There

---

*This had been the Peavy property, which the pre-Authority Board of Northside Hospital Association could have bought 10 years before at $6,500 an acre but could not afford at that time.

**In 1978 Northside began the first hospital-based Home Health Service in Georgia; the Tumor Registry and Barry Silverman's Cardiac Rehabilitation Center opened; and the speech pathologist arrived. Blue Cross/Blue Shield instituted a Utilization Review Program effective January 1, 1978, to control hospital costs by paying only for hospital stays they deemed medically necessary. Chris Clark became a member of their board. In 1979 the Convalescent Center opened, with John McCoy as director.

had begun a subtle shift in the attitude and relation-ship of the administrator and his staff (more so in the case of Bart Miller than George Simpson*) towards physicians, who increasingly would be regarded as "them." There was becoming more, not less, need for strong medical staff leadership (without confrontation) in a setting which did not seem to encourage the fast emergence of real leaders.

John Hall (1973-74) and David Cohen (1974-75) were two medical staff chairmen who became (and have remained) sensitized to the notion that "eternal vigilance is the price of liberty," and that part of their responsibility was to insure that neither they nor the remainder of the medical staff became complacent. The next four chairmen were more relaxed. Nature abhors a vacuum; there was a power vacuum which the administrator quietly began to fill.

Clark, his long-time secretary Marilyn Current, and key staff were invited to all meetings of the exec-utive committee of the medical staff, and they attended regularly. He even occasionally helped write the minutes, when the physician was tied up. Tom Gable (staff head in 1980-81) recalled when Clark even revised his own minutes after they had been sub-mitted. Chris was intimately familiar with the work-ings of the medical staff and with all its personalities.

As Gable recalled, during the first five to six years after he came to Northside, there was a distinct sense of camaraderie, and the doctors were very protective of "our" hospital. After Scottish Rite (opened in 1976) and St. Joseph's (in 1978) welcomed and encouraged their use by Northside physicians, administration became more openly turf-protective. Conflicts, usually minor, with individuals or sections in the medical staff arose more often. The staff became concerned about

complaints and unmet needs which it felt the board wasn't listening to (or never heard), and physician ref-erences to Northside as "our" hospital waned.

Actually, the hospital was trying mightily to get it all together and heavily involved the medical staff in planning a badly needed major expansion.

◆

The Eighties: Expansion Blues

In 1979 Northside had a bed shortage again, the highest use (by 5-6%) of any hospital in the city, and it was recommended that the medical staff member-ship be closed to new applicants for a period of one year. The hospital's experienced Utilization Review system functioned well, extending even to OB. It was recommended that OB admissions be limited. By 1980 the bed problem became critical. Outside the hospital a red light meant that there were no beds available; a green light, which was less frequent, was good news. It was recommended that Gynecological (Gyn) patients be moved to another hospital; Ed Bowen suggested all Gyn patients be operated upon or otherwise treated at St. Joseph's. Arthur Booth sug-gested a tradeoff allowing Gyn patients to be located at St. Joseph's in return for acquiring new OB beds at Northside. Aware of the situation, Shallowford made plans to open a small OB section.**

In the end, the hospital decided to sit tight and proceed with the planning of the second major expan-sion, guaranteeing the OB-Gyn section that the expansion would take care of their needs as well as everyone else's. Northside, it seemed, was destined to play catch-up once more.***

In 1980 planning had begun in earnest for the much-talked about expansion program designed to

---

*Miller, a fresh graduate of Georgia State, came to Northside to do his residency in administration. At Clark's invitation, he became director of support services. Simpson, who came from the Medical College of Georgia, had the same job there as he would have at Northside — director of ancillary services.

**In September 1979 the medical staff had 264 active members, 47 associate, 104 provisional — a total of 415 active members. The total number of members recorded on the staff roster was 748, but this also included 307 on the "courtesy" staff, 24 "consulting" and 2 "honorary."

***In 1981, the following year, HCA (Hospital Corporation of America) representatives came to Chris Clark with a proposal to build a 200-bed Women's Pavilion on Northside property, in the employee parking lot on the other side of Hollis Cobb Drive. (He did not know whether it came directly from HCA or was initiated by some of the obstetricians.) This would not be a free-standing building, with its own support system, but would simply be a satellite of Northside Hospital, with Northside supplying the back-up support services. The authority showed no interest at all in this proposal because it provided no discernible benefit for Northside. Besides, by that time the plans for OB expansion had already been completed and Planning Agency approval of the overall expansion was already being sought. Furthermore, an CON application by HCA would likely conflict with Northside's own CON application.

    Arthur Booth recalls that the subject of a proposed HCA-built Women's Pavilion was also brought up at a medical staff meeting by Charles Rogers, Mitch Sealey, and perhaps others. This latter time it was proposed as a self-contained, free-standing facility where the Medical Quarters building is now located. Booth says he and others thought it would be a disastrous idea because there was no adequate support system envisioned, and such a pavilion would need the kind of services and organizational backup, as well as spe-cialty physician support, that only the main hospital could provide. The matter was closed for the remainder of the decade.

take care of all of Northside's pent-up needs. No one could have anticipated the nightmare of frustrating delays, primarily due to the playing out of legal challenges by competitors, and that construction would not be completed until 1987. In the fall of 1981 came the first announcement that the CON application had been held up.

The exhausting legal battles began with objections by Shallowford, which was simply a competitor, and by the competing CON applications of the three would-be developers of the North Fulton hospital, which, in turn, were competing with Northside's CON application for expansion. To complicate and prolong the situation, the losers then sued to appeal the decision which was favorable to Northside. The appeal process consumed more months.

In 1983 the Court of Appeals finally ruled in favor of Northside's expansion program, although actual construction did not begin until 1984.

▿▿▿▿

There was one other significant development in 1983: to help reduce hospital reimbursements from Medicare, the government introduced the DRG (Diagnostic-Related Group) formula, paying a flat rate for a particular condition, based on the average cost of treating the condition and regardless of the actual cost incurred by the hospital (or the patient). Most hospitals moaned over this new restriction, but Clark felt like celebrating; Northside had a windfall. He said it was one of the few hospitals in the eastern United States which made money off the DRG system, because its actual charges were lower than its rate of reimbursement under Medicare.

But hospital costs rose and the government learned how to fine-tune the system. Chris said that after three years nobody could make any money.

One of the main reasons for Northside's coming out ahead in responding to the government's regulations was its excellent Utilization Review system, structured to shorten hospital stay, born out of necessity because of the bed shortage.*

Related to utilization review, Clark's involvement as one of the founding members of the Atlanta Healthcare Coalition (later named the Atlanta Healthcare Alliance) in the early '80s has remained a special source of pride for him. This was an outgrowth and spin-off of the Atlanta Chamber of Commerce's cost containment committee.

Ordinarily, physicians and hospital administrators are not permitted in such business-based coalitions, but Chris was invited to be on the board because he was and had been an employer, and had previously participated primarily as an employer. He was fond of saying that Northside was different in that it was always part of the solution and not part of the problem. He served at least 5 or 6 years, from the time it was created until a year after he left Northside.

One of the first projects of the Alliance was to offer a good, well-run utilization management program that any employer could use, regardless of their insurance. Medicare required utilization review (UR) and Northside had already been a pilot for Medicare UR. Clark chaired the UR committee for both the Alliance and for Blue Cross, which had decided to do UR. At Northside, Clark says, nurse Shirley Davis and his assistant, George Simpson, knew utilization management as well as anyone, anywhere. By avoiding unnecessary service, they were able to keep the unit price down, saving money for employers, patients and insurers.

▿▿▿▿

The expansion construction, which had begun in 1984, took forty months to complete. Although the hospital announced that it was fully operational during that time, some parts of the hospital were disrupted much more than others and a number of physicians began taking their patients elsewhere.

My own department, radiology, which underwent complete reconstruction over a three-year period, had the look and feel of a war zone, with plaster falling around patients and personnel. The frequent rat-a-tat-tat of drilling made people flinch, there was no place to sit and no place to hide. It was a total turn-off. We felt sorry for the patients, sorry for their

---

*There were three other factors: (1) its bed occupancy was high (but overall would shrink 14% from '82-'83 to '83-'84. In 1984 occupancy rates in Atlanta-area hospitals plunged an average 5.4%, leaving an average of 39% of the area hospital beds vacant, according to the state planning agency); (2) a variety of factors contributing to lower hospital costs (e.g., the substitution of generic drugs by the pharmacy committee, the large amount of outpatient work performed in radiology and the laboratory, ambulatory surgery, and Home Health Services allowing earlier discharge); and (3) for the first three years the DRGs had a uniform rate for all hospitals. The importance of cost accounting was proved.

doctors and sorry for ourselves. And to top it off, we had never been happy with the plans, which had been repeatedly changed by administration.

In 1986 the expansion construction was still grinding away. In June the new ICU opened; in July the OR, outpatient surgery, post-partum and nursery; and in October the ground floor and admissions. After 16 years the physicians finally had their own lounge where they could grab a quick bite to eat without having to go through the busy cafeteria line. The Institute for Cancer Control opened under Dale McCord. The hospital joined Sun Alliance, which enabled it to save money and lower costs by bulk purchasing of equipment and supplies.

Board Chairman Tom Rains sold the board on the idea of building the controversial second doctors' building (now known as the 980 Doctors' Centre). Construction began in late 1984 near the same time as construction on the long-delayed major expansion.

The building was initially unpopular with many on the medical staff because: (1) there were already more doctors on the staff than the hospital could accommodate, and building would simply encourage more doctor competitors from outside the area; (2) the hospital had expressed its intention to have close ties with the members of the medical staff, but it could not enter joint ventures without giving up its non-profit status, and it was unwilling to make any concessions to its physician tenants; and (3) the hospital seemed to care only for its own welfare. Cited as an example, it refused to renew the lease of a private radiology group not connected with the hospital which had been tenants in the first doctors' building for many years, in order to give the hospital its own outpatient radiology monopoly. Furthermore, construction coincided with the onset of the big fund-raising campaign for the major expansion program, and the hospital was simultaneously pushing for a large contribution from physicians.

At the time Rains came on the authority, in 1978, he had been a banker and owned his own property management company. Clark said he was "a real leader, very aggressive, who took positions and sold positions and stood behind them." He felt hurt by the less than enthusiastic welcome he received by sections of the medical staff during the fund-raising campaign. The projected contribution from physicians was lowered to $500,000, of which 94% was raised in signed pledges in 1985 from the active staff membership of 498 and 302 courtesy staff. The Doctors' Centre turned out to be quite successful. According to Clark, when Rains' term on the Authority ended in 1986, he and his wife went to ministerial school and now both are ministers.

In 1983-84 hospitals became seriously interested in marketing, and the public relations personnel were saddled with marketing responsibilities. In 1984 the Georgia Society for Hospital Marketing and Public Relations had added the "marketing" portion of its title. Realizing "we always have to be aggressive about developing tomorrow's source of patients; we can't rest on our laurels," in 1984 Clark hired Ron Everett, a strategic planner who had been at Kurt Salmon, the company which had produced Northside's second major expansion plan, to head its first Planning and Marketing office.*

At the urging of the author, Northside proposed to St. Joseph's (and Scottish Rite) a joint Magnetic Resonance Imaging program and installation, as a good fresh start in a policy of close cooperation on The Hill. This began a series of prolonged negotiations between Northside and St. Joseph's, with the administrators Clark and Wheeler primarily involved, although a whole committee participated. Initially the agreement was that the installation would be on St. Joseph's property, since space was available. (Scottish Rite was willing to do what the other two could agree upon.)

In 1985 Northside employed the consulting firm of Cresap, McCormick and Paget to make recommendations for long-range planning. They were excited by the unusual opportunity presented by the presence of three first-rate hospitals located next to each other in a prime location in one of Atlanta's major future growth areas.**

---

*In June 1984 the in vitro fertilization program pathologist Charles Garrison and gynecologist/reproduction specialist Camran Nezhat, based at the hospital, was approved by the Executive Committee of the medical staff. The same month obstetrician/reproduction specialist Hilton Kort delivered the first "test tube" baby to be conceived in a clinic in Georgia. The baby girl's parents were Janet and Ray Caputo. Ray was a dermatologist at Northside. (It was the year after Kort, and his associate, Joe Massey, as investigators, had submitted an "InVitro Fertilization/Embryo Transfer" research protocol to Northside's Institutional Review Board.) In 1984 the hospice became operational, with John McCoy as director.

**Separately, an ad hoc Joint Planning Committee had been formulated to explore opportunities for the hospitals to work closely together. Clark reported the three hospitals discussed having joint ventures under one corporation. There were 15 task forces, one of which suggested restructuring.

At that time the administrators of Northside and St. Joseph's did not completely trust each other, and the medical staffs were wary of both. Knowing this, the MCNA spearheaded a movement that brought the hospitals together in a Tri-Hospital/MCNA Association with a board of directors composed of board members from each of the three hospitals plus three board members from the MCNA. With the CEOs as ex-officio members, these began meeting monthly.

They began on non-controversial subjects: central application processing, joint identification, MARTA end station, joint security, parking lot access cards, joint landscaping, medical waste disposal and hospice. Nothing major was accomplished during the remainder of Clark's tenure or that of his successor, except that in 1986 a joint venture with St. Joseph's on MRI was approved by both hospitals. In 1986 it was still supposed to be located at St. Joseph's.

In the meantime, Parry Soder, the head of radiology at St. Joseph's, had purchased an MRI unit of his own, financed by physician-investors from both hospitals who doubted whether the administrations and boards of both hospitals would ever jointly agree on anything of major importance and became impatient waiting for this revolutionary new technology. Soder and company placed it in a private building near St. Joseph's; both administrators said such an independent move by the radiologists of either hospital was forbidden, under the terms of their understanding, punishable by firing, but it was done anyway. (It quickly became quite successful for its investors and, indirectly, for St. Joseph's, because it drew these physicians into closer ties with St. Joseph's.) Embarrassed, St. Joseph's agreed to share in the installation of a joint-venture MR unit on Northside property, which was finally done in 1987, in space created next to the radiology department. Unfortunately, the joint-venture Diasonics unit, purchased three years earlier, was already almost outdated by advances in technology in the interim. (Eventually both hospitals purchased their own new units and St. Joseph's purchased the installation from Soder and company.)

In 1986 the Tri-Hospital Association/MCNA agreed to employ the services of Cresap et al (Gar Fritts was its principal agent) to research joint venture possibilities.

▄▄▄▄▄

One of the concerns among physicians and board members about being sponsored by the county-based hospital authority was that of "being beholden" to the county commissioners. After all, the original debt was guaranteed by the commissioners. If Northside defaulted, they would be held responsible. In such event, they could take Northside over, and give it, on right of first refusal, to Grady. Although unlikely, the spectre was there. And every time Northside wanted to expand it had to get the approval of the commissioners and of Grady because they were signatories. Relieved of this responsibility, the commissioners were much more comfortable with Northside, and inclined to give it a freer hand in directing its own destiny.

The board would give names of nominees of future board members to the commissioners, who would ordinarily give back the same names, with or without any additions, to the board who would then make their final selection. The board was never sure it would get back the people it asked for, and sometimes it did not. On several occasions the commissioners came up with people out of the blue. Commissioner Goodwyn "Shag" Cates, for example, decided he wanted his brother Charles on the board. He sent the board three names, one of whom was Charles Cates; no one had ever heard of the two others, although they lived in the county. Lea Richmond says the other two were picked from the names of men imprisoned in the county stockade. Charles Cates's name appears on the board roster, but he never attended a meeting and he was never reelected.

One year, the commissioners told Chris and the board informally that it needed to have a black board member. When the board's next slate was all white, they were returned a slate of three black nominees. Of these they selected Jim Densler, a surgeon who understood issues related to his specialty. Later, when another vacancy on the board occurred, the board came up with Ellen Acquaviva, a public relations executive with her own firm, whom Clark had known in Leadership Atlanta, who came well recommended and was visible in the black business community. Densler and Acquaviva were excellent board members, Clark said, and attended the meetings faithfully. They spoke their own minds, neither had any axes to grind and neither ever used color as an issue.

Being tied to the county commission was never a major problem, Chris said, because the head of the County Commission, Michael Lomax was always fair. But this potential source of conflict was removed when the hospital bonds were refinanced in 1985. In this major bond issue, which funded the big expansion, the county no longer had to guarantee Northside's debt; it was now guaranteed by triple A bond insurance, for which Northside was willing and able to pay a premium.

〰〰

It was about this time that Chris did something which was not like him; he needlessly offended Scottish Rite. The SRCMC was excited about its new plans for a first-rate Pediatric Emergency Section, which was opening that year (1984), designed and equipped to handle serious emergencies. Chris was shown the plans for his comment. About a week or two afterwards, Northside announced the opening of its own new Pediatric Emergency Room (but one which had nothing to offer but its cosmetic appearance), and pediatrician Scott James agreed to pose in pictures of the room for the local papers.* No one at Scottish Rite ever commented publicly, but many of the medical/dental staff there remembered that incident for a long time, and Scottish Rite became less enthusiastic about working with Chris in cooperative efforts on The Hill.

〰〰

Chris: A Composite of Physician Impressions

One of the psychiatrists, a former head of the medical staff and former trustee, called Chris "enigmatic." It is true that his personality did not fit into a neat little package, but to a number of physician Clark-watchers who had interacted with the administrator over more than a decade, he was anything but. Over the years a profile emerged** which was consistent and fairly reliable in its predictability:

He was regarded as an excellent delegater, but he delegated responsibility without authority. Since he emphasized going through chain of command, his subordinates at times seemed more like buffers to keep him from exposure or having to make a decision until he felt like it rather than like expediters. He saw himself as a team player; but he was a team player only if he made the rules. He declared it ludicrous that anyone would think he would try to control the medical staff because it would be so counterproductive; but that increasingly was their perception, and, in some ways, that is exactly what he tried to do.

Matters were so structured that it was hard to pin down his personal accountability. His verbal agreements and understandings could not always be counted upon, and on the same matters it was difficult to get anything in writing.

He sometimes volunteered to take the blame on inconsequential matters, even when he was not at fault; but he rarely, if ever, admitted to making a mistake of any importance.

He never made a move until he was ready; but he expected a quick response.

He did not make the best use of consultants in that he used them more to accomplish what he directed them to do than to get their impartial feedback; this sometimes led to faulty decisions.

He understood that one of the tools of governance is fear; his subordinates*** were sometimes afraid to tell him what they really thought. Since he did not encourage impartial feedback, he did not always get the feedback he needed to make good decisions.

He always deferred to the authority, but the lay members of the authority, whose perspective and knowledge was based on what he told them and how he put it, often rubberstamped whatever he set up.

What is truth? Some of these perceptions of him and his style had implications for his relationship with the medical staff and for his performance as president and CEO, and affected his otherwise praiseworthy

---

*According to the article in *The North Fulton Extra* section of the *Atlanta Journal/Constitution* on July 3, 1984, the new room was part of the hospital's ongoing expansion program: "The room, especially designed to put tots at ease, features familiar stuffed animals, dolls, games, a rocking chair and a cheerful border around the ceiling."

**This composite is distilled from numerous interviews, in addition to recollections of previous expressions of opinion. Numerous graphic illustrations could be cited, but to do so would alter the spirit and tenor of this presentation.

***Ted Walker, Clark's long-time manager of pharmacy, recalled, "To many of us on the outside looking in, Chris seemed to surround himself with second level lieutenants and people who were not always of the highest caliber — 'yes men.' This seemed to work until the point when the hospital got larger than any one individual could handle. When that critical mass got into the 350-450 bed range, that style broke down mainly because of a lack of communication."

qualities. After a number of years some doctors became sensitized, and, as though provoked by an allergen, it took very little on Chris's part to produce a disproportionate response.

Most of the medical staff leaders during Clark's era had come to Northside when or after it opened and were no longer from the founder group. Three who played consequential roles during parts of this period and who are not referred to in other chapters deserve special mention — Arthur Booth, David Cohen and John Lee.

Booth was and is a committed, pithily outspoken general surgeon. He felt deeply that physicians with strong convictions about what was best for patient care and for the hospital had an obligation to stick their necks out and stand up and make a case for their beliefs. He will be remembered as founder of the Hospice of the South (1983), the first non-profit, non-sectarian hospice in the state, a cause for which has worked long and hard to raise funds and develop support. The hospice is scheduled to merge with the Visiting Nurses Association's Hospice of Atlanta into the largest non-profit hospice in Atlanta. Booth was a member of the Board of Trustees for five years (1982-1987).

Cohen was an energetic ENT surgeon, whose many and varied services to the medical staff and the hospital over more than 20 years have not been as widely appreciated as they deserve. Joining the medical staff in 1970, he became Chairman only three years later. Disappointed that he was never asked to serve on the Board of Trustees at Northside, he did serve on the Board at Scottish Rite (after being head of the medical staff there). He was head of Northside's Accreditation Committee eight years and was head of the Northside Foundation. He is a canny, respected entrepreneur and businessman. He and orthopedist Bill Collins (now a Northside trustee) are the general partners in physician partnerships which own the 993 Johnson Ferry Road medical office building complex and (with Stephen Blank) the new medical office building on the Alpharetta campus. Over the years Cohen has exerted considerable influence at Northside Hospital, much of it behind the scenes.

Lee, the soft-spoken gentlemanly neurologist, has been a calm, steady, moderating influence. Reflective, with a sense of historical perspective, he tried to see all sides of issues and situations. He was Chairman of the medical staff in 1984-1985 (a contentious period) and has been a member of the Board

of Trustees since 1987. He was former Chairman of the Education and Research committee and of the Institutional Review Board.

How Northside Did Not Build a Hospital in North Fulton

A Long-Range Planning Committee, initiated by the medical staff Executive Committee, made its formal report in July 1978. The last item in the report is of particular interest, since it was the first recorded reference to a possible North Fulton expansion:

"The remaining potential major element in the Long-Range Plan is the creation of a new satellite facility in the Roswell-Alpharetta area in North Fulton County. While this facility could not initially be planned to include any beds, adequate land would be acquired for expanse of bed facilities as they may become needed in the future. The initial scope of this facility would therefore provide for a variety of outpatient services, including ER, Diagnostic Radiology and Radiation Therapy and Outpatient Surgery. This long-range plan will be the subject of continuing review and amendment. This plan is jointly created by the medical staff, hospital departments and Hospital Authority of Fulton County — April 3, 1978."

Joe Aronoff might have become a Northside hero. About 1980, the Aronoff affair was the event that never happened, and that is why only a handful of people around there ever knew who he was or what he wanted to do for Northside.

Aronoff, who was chairman of the Fulton County Planning Commission for 12 years (he also had been on the Advisory Board at Scottish Rite), was also a land developer who worked for a wealthy Atlantan (who asks that his name not be used) as an adviser on real estate investments. Aronoff helped his boss purchase 1,000 acres of land at Webb Road and Union Hill Road in North Fulton County, across the expressway from what is now Windward Parkway. Bachelor Aronoff also had a vision.

As a developer, he had dreamed many times of making a unique contribution to the area. He could envision in North Fulton County a first-rate regional medical facility, a nursing home, a funeral home and a cemetery. As he discussed with his friend and fellow-developer Lea Richmond, III, this property gave him a chance to fulfill a dream as well as to enhance the value of the property. In addition, he had always liked Northside and had been on the zoning board when its application was approved.

According to Aronoff (substantiated by Lea Richmond, III) he proposed donating about 80 acres of the best land, with at least 1,000 feet of footage, requiring little or no grading at a nominal charge, virtually a donation (as I recall, the total amount was $15,000 or less) to Northside Hospital. The property would be used for Northside to build a satellite facility. There were no strings attached. The increase in value of the surrounding 920 acres would make this donation worthwhile. Lea Richmond, III, thought it was a good idea; Aronoff was introduced to Clark and made his proposal.

What happened? Joe Aronoff says, "All I know is that I never got an answer from Chris."

Chris Clark, who corroborates Aronoff's proposal, says he even went to see the property, but that, "It was a very unripe idea at that time. We had not included it in our strategic plans — it was right out of the blue. We did some financial feasibility studies. I talked about it at the authority meeting but couldn't get any interest. We had no remote idea of building anything in North Fulton." The August 21, 1980 minutes of the Executive Committee recorded: "Clark elaborated on the plans for expansion by the hospital and explained the position of the authority in not proceeding with plans for a hospital in the Roswell area."

Lea Richmond, III, recalls that at that time he heard two different versions of why the offer fell through. The "official word" feedback, he was told, was that Northside was almost obsessively committed to the urgently needed expansion already planned on its home property. The financial demands of that major building project were staggering, and Northside didn't want anything to jeopardize the State Planning Agency approval of its plans and its CON application. Northside was afraid that if it had accepted this offer, that acceptance would not have gone well with Pat Leit (one of the heads of SHPDA). The "real reason," he was told by others, was that the primary care physicians and obstetricians had all they could handle and

did not like the prospect of taking care of patients in two widely separated locations. Very recently, I called the unnamed owner, who did not want to talk about the incident. He did say he was not even aware an offer had been made.

Not more than a year or two later, Clark would look at North Fulton differently. In October 1981, Clark announced that its expansion program was delayed by legal challenges and court battles; in 1982 the bed situation at Northside remained critical, and the red light was usually on. There was almost constant overcrowding in the labor & delivery, nursery and post-partum areas.

Three hospital chains began sniffing around Roswell and Alpharetta. Previously some officials connected with Northside had privately assured representatives of those areas that in due time it would take care of their needs, but these rapidly growing communities began feeling like neglected stepchildren. They were not stupid; they saw Northside, despite its good intentions, having its hands full just trying to meet its own current needs. The three developers, who would have competing CON applications, went to the state planning agency and were told that no hospital was yet needed. But the community, which was already aroused, was revved up, by American Medical International (AMI), Hospital Corporation of America (HCA), and Physicians & Surgeons.

Clark recalls, "We were deep into the court battle when John Geppi (Northside's chief financial officer) and Ron Everett* (who would become the new head of Planning and Marketing) came to me one day and said, 'Those guys who are building those projects on paper at North Fulton are right. That is where the population is growing. We ought to be there. They are going to get approved whether we get approved or not. We ought to be there instead.' And I said, 'Gosh! You are exactly right.'

"We hit the ground running. We first talked through the issue of what the planning agency wanted to approve, and that was a satellite of Northside. They didn't want a free-standing total replication of a hospital. We found the site (where AMI North Fulton Regional Hospital is now located in Alpharetta)

---

*Everett had worked for Kurt Salmon Associates, the firm that did the original long-range planning resulting in the big expansion program; he had been the project manager. He came recommended by Pat Leit after he left Kurt Salmon. According to Clark, "He perceived the need, he had a database analysis and was able to put together a good case."

through a real estate developer and secured an option to buy a larger number of acres than they now have. We had schematic drawings done in Nashville to maintain secrecy, by an architect there who completely prepared the CON. It was an amazing crash project, done over a period of about two months. We came to the powers-that-be on the authority and medical staff and filled them in. We met with community leaders and switched a lot of their support over to Northside's doing it. We showed them what would happen with prices and costs, and how we could do it more efficiently and cost-effectively, starting out with a satellite first — servicing it from Northside so one would not have to duplicate a lot of the equipment and infrastructure. Even the politicians were behind it. At Northside the plans had all been tentatively preapproved, barring unexpected developments, in committee meetings and at the previous board meeting.

"We came to the authority for final approval — and were turned down flat! We were completely blind-sided. The board members simply came in, listened and voted. I think only two board members voted for it. One member of the medical staff [he would not tell me who it was] had gone to each member of the board, one at a time, and had said it was the wrong thing to do, that we needed to put our money and our efforts on this home site, and it would be disaster if we did otherwise."

Clark lists this as the second of his three major disappointments.*

The Beginnings of Managed Care in Atlanta and at Northside

A new development, potentially affecting future planning, was introduced at the medical staff's Executive Committee meeting in July 1979, when Chris Clark reported on his contacts with HMO's which had just begun arriving in Georgia. At that time Atlanta's medical community still looked down upon managed care as an inferior form of patient care and medical practice, and was quite wary of these intruders. Northside's physicians were no exception.

When Gordon Azar** took over as the new head of the medical staff in September 1979 (the same month Jack Marquis became head of the authority), he urged that any HMO proposal seriously considered by the hospital also be submitted to the Executive Committee of the medical staff. He emphasized that if a contract were to be entered into with an HMO, there would be no special privileges for the organization or its physician members. Its doctors would be required to be members of the Northside staff on the same basis, and with the same obligations, as any other physician on the staff.

In April 1984 the hospital presented programs about the possible formation of a PPO (Preferred Provider Organization) at Northside, involving both the hospital and the medical staff. Later that month the physicians formed an ad hoc committee for reorganization of the medical staff. John McCoy stressed the need to have a formal organization, separate from the official medical staff, to deal with PPO's (and other matters, such as DRG reimbursements) rather than depending upon the hospital — because an attorney named John Horty had asserted that the medical staff was legally inseparable from the hospital.

This meant that the administration could not work out arrangements between itself and the medical staff, or that the staff might have to accept whatever decisions the hospital made, including those made in its behalf. Two months later, the Northside Physicians Inc. was formed, with John McCoy, chairman and Tom Gable, vice chairman. It found that 104 of the physicians admitted over 80% of the patients at Northside, which could carry weight in discussions with administration. It was the first time the physicians had thought about their potential united

---

*A few physicians on the staff, like Jim Langford, said by the time Northside's administration really became gung ho about North Fulton, the community had been so aroused that it would not have been satisfied with anything less than the prospect of a full service hospital. AMI wound up building the hospital. Its CON application, originally turned down, was approved in February 1982 and the North Fulton Regional Hospital, which it was named, opened in November 1983. The physicians there were very unhappy with its first administrator, and that hospital had its share of problems. As predicted, it was initially too high priced and for some time was poorly utilized. At times in the '80s, it was said to be for sale, and Clark says he repeatedly tried to buy it. The perceptions of individual physicians concerning Clark's attitude on North Fulton have been varied; one former staff chairman was convinced he was clearly against it.

**He was the first chairman to make a heartfelt opening speech: "It is a rare moment in the life of a man when he has the opportunity of standing before his distinguished and respected colleagues to share with them a few of his personal feelings … We are a troubled profession in a troubled country in a troubled world … First and foremost, we must address ourselves to the ills of our profession and cure its internal diseases. For it is only by fortifying our profession from within that we will be able to withstand the onslaughts from without."

strength. In May 1984 Blue Cross/Blue Shield, the largest health insurer in Atlanta at that time, launched Atlanta's first PPO. It invited 49 metro Atlanta hospitals and free standing surgical clinics to submit bids for participation in the program. To be included on the "preferred provider" list for referrals, the facilities had to offer at least a 7% discount.

Chris Clark, on the board of Blue Cross at the time, thought that the extent of patient referral was problematic, but that it could be a good learning experience about PPO's and managed care, and so informed the board. Lea Richmond, who was a Northside trustee at that time, agreed it would be worthwhile as a learning experience, but also thought it a wise business move. He knew, however, that in those days "anything that smacked of control in medicine would be considered a dangerous thing." He says he advised the board: "Don't go to the medical staff; they are going to vote against it." Clark thought it necessary to receive medical staff approval, but thought he "could not bring it up before them unless there was the possibility of a deal," so he prepared a tentative proposal.

The Blue Cross proposal came up first at St. Joseph's, when their administrator, Ken Wheeler, brought it before the medical staff. They turned it down cold. Shortly thereafter their medical staff learned that Ken had already cut a deal with Blue Cross. From that point on, their medical staff never trusted Ken again.

By this time in Northside's history, a number of Northside physicians had grown less trustful of Clark. Since many were also on the staff at St. Joseph's, they also wondered whether Clark might have cut a deal. At Northside's general staff meeting speakers were impassioned. The thought of "discount medicine" offended them. Northside had prided itself that its hospital costs were already among the lowest in town; that didn't seem to matter to Blue Cross — all they seemed to want was "a discount." If one's charges were too high, they should be realistically lowered, not automatically discounted across the board. If this is what managed care was all about, surgeon Keith Quarterman intoned, "Don't let that camel get his nose under the tent!"

Northside's medical staff turned it down almost unanimously. Lea Richmond remembers he was the only doctor who voted for it. (Two years later, in July 1986, Northside did sign a contract with the Blue Cross/Blue Shield HMO, but without discounts.)

Dick Bibel, the hospital's financial department head, was down at Blue Cross with Clark's proposal for the authority's approval before the 5 p.m. deadline. At five minutes to 5:00 the board voted to turn down the PPO. Tom Gable recalls it was the only time he ever saw Clark sweat. The August 1, 1984 *Atlanta Journal* reported: "Among the 27 hospitals and surgical clinics not participating are Northside Hospital, West Paces Ferry Hospital and the three institutions operated by the Gwinnett Hospital Authority."

In the newspaper article reporting the results of the Blue Cross episode, Clark indicated he already had something else in mind. For several years he had been following the evolution and growth of managed care nationwide; he could now see it coming "like a large freight train." He conceived the idea of Southcare, an Atlanta-based PPO, with 50-50 ownership and governance by physicians and hospitals. It would be structured so that any insurance company or utilization management company could use it. He sold Charles Eberhardt, the administrator at DeKalb, on the idea and invited him and six other hospital CEO's to a meeting at DeKalb. The eight local hospitals (their charges were known to be among the lowest in town) and their medical staffs formed the PPO known as "Southcare," a name coined by the PR advisor. Now Southcare is the largest PPO in Atlanta.

~~~~~~

The Medical Center of North Atlanta (MCNA)*

The Medical Center of North Atlanta also had its beginnings in 1984, after some of the physicians had second thoughts concerning the Northside Physicians, Inc., which the doctors had hurriedly organized to protect themselves and their interests. Although it could be quite useful, it could easily be labelled by the hospital as partisan and confrontational. Its limitation to Northside's doctors could be divisive. It would be far better to spend the effort on a positive, upbeat

*Gordon Azar has spearheaded the MCNA and has remained its chairman. Napier ("Buck") Burson (Vice-Chairman), Lyndon Waugh (Secretary), and Richard Franco (Treasurer), on the initial board of Directors, have all remained active. Others on the original board were; Jim Alexander, Arthur Booth, Ernest Franklin, Tom Gable, Harold Harrison, Jud Hawk, Greg Knowlton, John Lee, Marty Moran, John McCoy, Ray Morrissy, Ed Rainey, Charles Rogers and Byron Williams. Earl Pennington and Rod Cabezas are among others more active in recent years.

organization which could bring the doctors from all three hospitals on The Hill together, help them with their common needs, and hopefully serve as the catalyst and bridge which would eventually bring all three hospitals together.

In July 1985 MCNA incorporated, inviting all physicians from the three hospitals: "to have a unified voice in influencing the future direction of health care in our community." MCNA, which is still in existence, has had two purposes: "(1) to be the physicians' advocate (and educator) in all matters of concern to our members and our profession, such as hospital relations, governmental regulations, third party payors, continuing medical education, quality, cost and access to health care, etc.; and (2) to bring our three hospitals together in a cooperative endeavor in the development of a superb medical center that will provide a complete spectrum of the highest quality of medical care from the beginning of life to its end." One of its most useful features for physicians has been its systematic reviews analyzing and comparing all submitted HMO and PPO contracts in conjunction with 18-point guidelines.

〰〰

Why Clark Nixed Northside's Restructuring (Giving Up the Authority Status)

As one of their planning and marketing strategies in the mid-'80s, a number of hospitals entered joint ventures with their medical staffs. Northside was prevented from doing so, even if it wanted to, unless it was willing to give up its non-profit status, because it was sponsored by a hospital authority. That was one of three reasons an increasing number of physicians and others felt that Northside should "get out from under the Authority" and restructure simply as a non-profit hospital, fully responsible for its own welfare. The second reason was that it could not expand into another county. The third was fear of the unknown. As long as it was nominally under the control of the county commissioners, it was conceivable that as MARTA made Northside more accessible from downtown Atlanta, Northside could become "The Grady of the North," subject to overflow indigent patients from downtown Grady Hospital and environs.

Clark pointed out that the hospitals which corporately reorganized to form joint ventures with their

medical staffs found that these turned out to be a lot less rewarding and/or had more problems (restraint of trade, self-referral, etc.) than anticipated, and some changed back to their old form. He also pointed out that the authority had some advantages which were not sufficiently appreciated: (1) exemptions from property taxes, sales taxes and the requirement of the wage and hour law; (2) exemption from the National Labor Relations Board, i.e., the hospital employees are not subject to unionization; (3) exemption from OSHA, an expensive set of occupational and health standards (Clark said some of these were unnecessary); and (4) the right of eminent domain (which prevented MARTA from arbitrarily determining MARTA's intended route in relation to Northside's property).

The expectation that the hospital would provide a certain amount of care for indigent patients was a Hill-Burton, not an authority, requirement. Clark said the fact that Northside had never been turned down on a CON application or zoning or offset variance was not due to Northside's authority status, but it did not hurt.

In addition to Clark, Ferdinard Buckley (on the board from 1982 to 1990, board chairman in 1987-89), was adamantly against ending the authority connection, which is part of the reason corporate reorganization did not take place until after Buckley and Clark both left.

〰〰

Towards the End

There was a distinct change in the complexion of medical care at Northside in the latter half of the '80s. The prolonged, arduous, costly process of expansion, compounded by delays and legal wrangling inflicted stress, inconvenience and dissatisfaction on patients, physicians and employees. St. Joseph's and other nearby hospitals had empty beds, and user-friendly facilities. They were only too glad to welcome the patient and the physician and accommodate their needs.

Over the 40 months of construction, from 1984 to 1987, practice patterns changed and many patients and their physicians saw no reason to go back to Northside. A heavy debt service, a chassis that was now oversized for its needs, and dropping bed occupancy almost brought Northside to its knees financially. St. Joseph's clearly had the upper hand on The Hill and Northside's trajectory was tilted downward. According to Chris's public word, everything was just fine.

One of the straws that broke the camel's back, according to David Cohen, was when Clark made a special deal with one of the HMOs (Ameriplan), giving preferential rates to attract business, after he had promised the medical staff he would not. Clark says this was not a breech of trust, as some physicians had presumed, because it involved only the hospital, with no physician obligation. He said some Northside doctors were already involved with Ameriplan and did not want Northside to be ruled out as a preferred provider. In fact, Clark is proud of his Ameriplan negotiations. He completed them after he formally resigned from Northside in September 1987, in what he describes as "the first hospital capitation deal in Georgia, which made a lot of money for Northside."

Clark also pushed perhaps too hard for Northside's status as a trauma center until the medical staff finally decided it could not truly be in the trauma system.

Surgeon John Harvey, in charge of the Trauma Committee, had special training and experience as a traumatologist. In 1986 the medical staff's Executive Committee voted to pursue a trauma center at Northside, but there was subsequently an honest but heated difference of opinion within the surgical section whether it had the manpower to support such a commitment. Northside's general surgeons would take care of Northside's own patients, no matter what, it was said, but they were reluctant to undertake a higher level (II) of commitment. The number of qualified general surgeons whose practices were not fully at Northside were cooler to the trauma center idea than some general surgeons who worked almost exclusively at Northside. They outnumbered the latter and threatened to resign if the issue were forced. Furthermore, some of Northside's orthopedists were already super-busy and did not want to get involved. At that time Northside's ER was sometimes dumped upon (such as by episodes of indigent or AIDS patients being brought there from the middle of faraway Decatur). Clark was frustrated because he felt that he was responsible for making it happen. He invited some young trauma doctors from Georgia

Baptist that Dr. Dale McCord had recommended to make application to join the staff at Northside, but that went over like a lead balloon. In January 1987, the general surgeons withdrew support from the trauma center, and in August 1987 the Executive Committee asked that Northside's name be withdrawn from consideration as a level II trauma center.

Clark considers the trauma center and the controversy that was sparked by it to be his third biggest frustration at Northside.

There also had been, in David Cohen's words "chaos and turmoil in dealing with in-house physicians (including repeatedly trying to force new contracts) and other doctors." But there was no trust and almost no new contracts, and things kept churning. Because of the continued unrest, general distrust and the extreme unhappiness of the in-house physicians, Cohen convened a meeting of medical staff chairmen, past and future. They had additional meetings; the consensus was, unless things improved, Clark had outlived his usefulness to Northside. (Looking back, Ted Walker says, "The conflicts that Chris encountered with the medical staff became legendary and, I guess, led to his demise [sic].")

The other straw involved alteration of nurses' pay. Northside prided itself on being an innovator, but when it came to wages and salaries, "we were always a wage follower," as Clark put it, adopting the usual policies of the other hospitals. To cut costs, the hospital announced "compression" of nurses' pay, narrowing the differential between the top pay for the most experienced nurses, and the bottom pay for those on entry level. Predictably, the nurses strenuously objected and, according to Clark, one nurse spokesperson threatened a strike if it were not corrected. Clark immediately hired a firm with a specialist in wage and hour work to help resolve the situation. He said the consultant came back with a report that the nurses were right, the "compression" was too great. A compromise was worked out, he said, which the board put into effect and the issue went right away.

Cohen recounted a different scenario. When he brought his patient back from surgery one morning, there was no nurse in the recovery room; the head of the recovery room was in the main operating room. There were no other nurses around. Cohen was told,

Marilyn Current, Chris Clark, and Linda Clark

"The nurses are staying out today." It was an unannounced strike. He was told the nurses were "basically unhappy with working conditions, salaries and how (they) were treated by administration."

Cohen felt, "We can't go on this way." After preliminary calls, which were not helpful (Lea Richmond, for example, was out of town), he wrote to Ferdinard Buckley, chairman of the board, on behalf of the past leadership of the medical staff. Buckley paid attention. The same group of medical staff leaders met again.

Arthur Booth, Larry Stone and Cohen made a trip to see Michael Lomax, chairman of the Fulton County Commissioners and presented a full bill of particulars over a number of issues. Lomax listened, asked questions and then called Buckley. Within a week Clark officially resigned.*

Actually, Clark had already submitted his resignation a month earlier, in August, to Buckley. At age 48, he felt he had been in hospital management long enough (the last 16 of the 25 years were spent at Northside), his "political capital" at Northside was mostly spent and it was time to move on. Buckley told him to wait until September, so that it would not appear that he was leaving because of the trauma center outcome.

Between his resignation and his departure in the spring of 1988, he did something which was very characteristic — he prepared an exceptionally detailed briefing guide for his successor.

---

*After leaving, he joined the Atlanta office of Heidrick & Struggles, an international executive search firm, where some of his clients are in the healthcare field.

~~~~

Although there are no landmark accomplishments to stamp his legacy, Clark says he is especially proud that he stuck to his same eight guiding principles* until the day he left. "That is what the big picture was; you had it tattooed on the inside of your eyelids and you read it even when you blinked. We wanted to exceed patients' expectations…"

David Cohen summed up Chris's tenure this way: "He was there during the best years of Northside. He was a good caretaker in that he watched carefully what came in and what went out; all his efforts were dedicated toward the day-to-day operation. This approach worked well in the early years, but he had no vision and no guiding philosophy. He did not create all the major problems we ran into, but he lost the confidence and trust of the medical staff, and we were convinced that he was not the person to lead us out of them."

That Chris Clark served as administrator for 15 years is itself a testimonial. During his era, hospital administration became a progressively harder and more complex job. While he evolved into a controversial figure, it is fair to say that in the hindsight of the '90s he has been looked upon with increased understanding, respect and even affection.

---

*"Follow the medical staff's lead. Respect their principles. Treat physicians as the hospital's best customers; never try to compete with them. Always stay ahead of mandatory requirements. Keep costs and charges low. Make the hospital highly reliable, productive and safe. Make the hospital an enjoyable place to work. Be innovative and on the cutting edge as an organization, fresh and alive and turned on."

CHAPTER

18

The Era of the Go-Go Administrator (1988-1992)

In the opinion of Northside's search committee, Ohio-born Donald H. Hutton, age 44, presented himself well, although he was not the first choice for administrator of the three candidates proffered by the headhunter group Witt and Associates. Hutton had been in the same capacity for the previous 3-1/2 years at Cabell Huntington Hospital, a 322-bed hospital in Huntington, West Virginia, a coal and railroad town of about 61,000 on the Ohio River.

There he had led conversion of that hospital from a public institution which answered to city and county governments, to a private, not-for-profit hospital — a change which he called, "probably the greatest accomplishment of my career."* The need for restructuring had risen high on Northside's list,** and Hutton's experience in that area could be a big plus.

Hutton, who had been praised as imaginative and energetic, said he has also been described as an aggressive person who likes to get things done.

Hutton says that when he came to Northside, the board gave him three basic tasks: stabilize the hospital financially, get it out from under the authority and restructure it as a private, non-profit community hospital and, as soon as these were accomplished, reposition Northside for changes and reforms expected in the health care delivery system in this country.

To complete the three tasks, Hutton judged that a large portion of his time and energy in the near future would have to be spent in building relationships with the political and business communities. "I knew I had to be outside. I could not possibly do that and run the hospital simultaneously. So Scott Malaney was recruited. [Hutton had worked with his younger friend and fellow-golfer at the St. Lawrence Hospital in Michigan.] I was looking for someone I could trust, without ever thinking about it again, with the operations of the hospital."

At Michigan State, Malaney graduated with a B.A. in Business Administration and then an M.A. in Labor and Industrial Relations. "He had the ability; we worked well together; there would be no second guessing. Malaney brought in some people, such as Heather Fritzler, in charge of human resources, and he kind of built his own team."

Besides Malaney as COO, Hutton considers three other people key on his team: Chris Press, "Mr. Spock," in charge of planning and marketing, who came out of a large Catholic system in Cincinnati; Bob Quattrocchi, chief financial officer, who was already at Northside; and Ken Kenton, in charge of the Foundation and fund-raising (see Appendix), who was discovered at Emory.

---

*Hutton started his professional career as a pharmacist. Finishing his graduate training in hospital administration at Xavier University in 1971, his first full-time job as an assistant administrator was at the Medical Center of Princeton, New Jersey. He was then attracted to the Wesson Memorial, a 300-bed teaching hospital in Springfield, Massachusetts, as chief operating officer (COO). There he became the CEO when three out of the four hospitals in the city decided to merge into a 1,000-bed hospital. After four or five years at Wesson, he became the COO and executive vice president at the 535-bed St. Lawrence Hospital in Lansing, Michigan. After five years there, where, he said, he turned the hospital around, he was attracted to the Cabell Huntington, a major teaching hospital in West Virginia. He had also turned that hospital around, he said, when he learned of the opening at Northside. Witt assured the board that he had had no major problems at Cabell. Later it was learned that difficulties he experienced there would recur at Northside.

**The restrictions of the authority's public status had prevented it from forming joint ventures to build its own clinics and limited its options in competing with other local hospitals and outpatient medical facilities. It was not allowed to operate outside of Fulton County. Other local authority-sponsored hospitals, such as DeKalb General, Kennestone and Cobb General, had already made that transition.

Although he discounts it as a factor, Hutton's modus operandi undoubtedly contributed to his subsequent problems with the medical staff. "My management style is one of recruiting and retaining good, trained people, supporting them in their effort, but not telling them what to do. Good people know what their overall job responsibilities are and they'll go out and find a way to do it." His was in sharp contrast to Chris Clark's style of total control and direction.

Scott Malaney agrees that Hutton was a deliberately hands-off manager, trusting the people he hired to the point of his own risk. As Hutton's long-time friend and business associate, Malaney says he was given an unusual breadth and depth of autonomy for a COO. For example, it was he who recruited, selected and hired the head of marketing and planning as well as the chief financial officer, and they both reported to him. Given the responsibility for "kind of the whole shooting match," he loved the opportunity, but felt he was often doing more than he should, and told Hutton so. One of the CEO's mistakes, Malaney said, was that "he liked to do the community thing so much that he put himself too far removed or too little involved, until it was too late. In addition to the fact that a lot of physicians didn't like him or didn't understand him, they were frustrated because he wasn't here very much." Because Hutton sensed many people were uncomfortable with him, Malaney says, at times he relied heavily on his COO as his public emissary.

Ted Walker, the long-term chief of the pharmacy section who was tapped by Hutton to head the expansion program in Alpharetta, in North Fulton County, recalls, "Don was and is a free spirit type of guy who would go from mountain top to mountain top, leaving the particulars of how to achieve some particular feat to those whom he worked with. At times this was extremely exciting and at other times extremely difficult because it was sometimes necessary to bring him back into reality and focus on the needs of the moment.

"Don was much more open in his management style than Chris. In Clark's day there was more of a military reporting scheme, whereas under Hutton some individuals were given so much freedom that, in many cases, they actually wrote their own job description and designed their own place in the organization."

Whereas Clark prided himself on not being a risk-taker (particularly where Northside's finances were concerned), Hutton considered an integral part of his job to be an entrepreneur — a role he enjoyed — and that he should stick his neck out and take calculated risks on behalf of the hospital. He assumed that no matter how careful one is, mistakes, including errors in judgment and decision-making, will be made and simply come with the territory. Consequently, when he felt it was the better part of valor and did not damage himself appreciably to do so, he freely admitted when he had been wrong. Clark, who was overall more meticulous and circumspect in his planning, always doing his own homework, made few blunders; curiously, when things went wrong, his fine hand in them was hard to find.

Sociable, Hutton was geared to a high public profile. Like Clark, he was a board member of Atlanta Healthcare Alliance, the business community's organization which centers its time dealing with healthcare issues relating to themselves as employers. How to deal with rising costs was constantly on the agenda. With the attitude that what was good for the community would be good for Northside, he was found acceptable to the corporate members of the Alliance. There he had both an opportunity for input and access to knowledge of where managed care was going.* Hutton also served as chairman of the Georgia Hospital Association and president of the Atlanta Chamber of Commerce North Branch.

〰〰〰

The new administrator and his mission were soon viewed somewhat differently by leaders of the medical staff. They had eagerly looked forward to working closely with him to help insure that he would indeed, as one said, "run the best damn hospital in the city." It soon became clear, they said, that Hutton was not deeply interested in the daily operations of the hospital; in fact, he did not appear comfortable in that role at all and made no great effort to familiarize himself with the details of the overall operation. He even had no more than a passing concern about the QI (Quality Improvement) program. At first they excused all that, but at the time of the periodic, always important JCAH (Joint Commission for Accreditation of

---

*In 1993, when Hutton was no longer administrator at Northside, he was head of the Atlanta Healthcare Alliance. By this time no hospital officials or physicians were allowed to be in the Alliance.

Hospitals) survey and inspection, his relative inattention and unexpected lack of interest (in contrast to his predecessor, Chris Clark) was unsettling to those who had to work hard to prepare for it. This served as a stimulus to look at the new CEO more closely.

They saw a pattern. At first glance this was not much different than Hutton and his managers had described, but they had a different interpretation, one which did not bode well: Hutton basically preferred being outside the hospital, loved his high public profile, making contacts at meetings and on the golf course, and focusing on the "big picture" in health care, something of potentially larger scope than Northside itself. The hospital was too humdrum, tedious, time-consuming. He liked throwing out new ideas and new projects and being where the action was. He liked living on the edge. His "open management style" was not really management at all but, instead, an excuse for abdication of as much direct responsibility as he could dispense with. He was always looking for something to glorify what he was doing which would offset the fact that he was not at the hospital. They concluded, with a sinking feeling, that he had no personal commitment or attachment to Northside per se, and some of the physicians separately arrived at the impression that Hutton looked upon Northside as a stepping stone to something higher, possibly in the national scene. They would wait and see.

▼▼▼▼

The first two challenges — financial turnaround and restructuring — were completed on schedule according to Hutton. When the new CEO came in 1988, Northside was economically hard-pressed due to an expansion program which took more than four years to complete, with gross revenues of $134 million but net earnings of only $1.7 million. By 1992, revenues doubled to $272 million, with a bottom line of $14 to $15 million. Hutton states that during his tenure Northside was the only hospital in Atlanta that had an increase in admissions and an increase in patient days.* With his revamped management team, he attributes much of the credit for turning around Northside's economic profile to his and Northside's becoming more heavily involved in managed care, which he considered the inevitable wave of the near future. Others agree, but felt Northside lost some of its soul in the process.

How was restructuring accomplished? Hutton declared, "Over time we convinced the county commissioners that it was something the hospital needed in the changing world of health care. At the same time, we showed them it was to their benefit as elected officials to support this, since this would eliminate the liability associated with being a member of an authority from affecting the future of their political careers. Then we built safeguards into a lease, which the county retains, which would prevent the non-profit corporation from doing something they didn't want it to do. So they had the best of all worlds."

There was also some good old-fashioned horse trading,** one result of which was that Morehouse, a predominantly black medical school in Fulton County, would receive, no strings attached, $100,000 each year in perpetuity. Eyebrows were raised in several quarters at this odd announcement because (a) Morehouse had no connection with Northside, (b) surplus funds at Northside had always been hard to come by, and (c) this gratuity sounded like a king's ransom.

*Actually, this was true for four straight years (1987-1991), but in 1992 there was a 10.8% drop. In 1992 there was a generalized decrease in hospital census, both in Atlanta and nationally, which has continued in 1993. Depending upon which figures one chooses to count, one could get a different perspective: In 1990, bed occupancy rates (a.k.a. hospital census) at Northside dipped to 65%, compared to 87% in 1986 and 92.7% in 1984. Much of this apparent discordance was due to more rapid patient turnover, a trend which is also reflected nationally.

CFO Bob Quattrocchi points out that the bed census is a function of the number of patient admissions and the length of stay, and that hospital bed occupancy rates are less indicative of hospital activity than they used to be. For example, at Northside in 1993, the number of admissions remains about the same as last year, but the average length of stay has decreased 10%. Thus far this slack in hospital activity (except for OB, which remains constant) has been compensated for by the growing utilization of outpatient services. The gross revenue for the past 12 months is about $300 million; 30% of this has come from outpatient services. Hutton did not mention that John Geppi, the able CFO whom he had inherited from Clark, was partly responsible for Northside's financial turnaround. Geppi resigned during Hutton's tenure; he never said why, and the circumstances are not known. Observers close to the scene felt it may have been that Hutton made some financial commitments on behalf of the hospital without consulting with and/or receiving the approval of the CFO. Both Geppi and his successor, Quattrochi, received uniformly high marks for their capabilities and both kept out of medical politics.

**Another part of the agreement was that a certain amount of indigent care and other non-reimbursable services would continue to be provided by Northside to residents of the county.

Hutton had a simple explanation. The commissioners thought the hospital did in fact owe them and the county something substantial for their support and backing of Northside over the years, even though tax dollars were not involved. The board agreed, and Hutton proposed it be a special fund to support the training of primary care physicians. The commissioners wanted to know how this would be accomplished. Hutton's idea was to put the money into medical schools — Emory, in DeKalb County, and Morehouse, in Fulton County. The commissioners agreed, except that Fulton County was the only one they had to deal with politically, so it would have to be Morehouse. They suggested "in perpetuity." After all, $100,00 is no small change, and from now on is a long, long time. Hutton's response: "No problem, because — with the time value of money — in 20 years $100,000 is going to be like $1,000. It will be of no value."

The officers and other leaders of the medical staff became miffed at Hutton's plan of reorganization, part of restructuring, which would give himself more power and would diminish the role of the medical staff. This issue became a turning point, crystallizing and hardening the attitude of many physicians towards the CEO.

The episode began, indirectly, with a rare meeting of in-house physicians from pathology, anesthesiology, radiology, neonatology and ER. They decided to share the cost of paying an attorney to look at the restructuring process, learn the facts and implications, and disseminate the information to other members of the medical staff in a special meeting. John Neeld, chairman of anesthesiology, chaired the meeting at the Galleria, attended by 75-80 physicians. Neeld and Gwynne Brunt, of radiology, did most of the legwork. Some aspects of the hastily called meeting were not ideal. Larry Stone, chairman of the medical staff, and John Lee, a physician member of the board, were out of town and some considered it a "rump group." Bill Collins cautioned, "We don't want to do anything outside our purview."

There was, however, a good representation of key medical players on such short notice, including Ed Bowen, the chairman-elect of the medical staff, both physician members of the board (Earl Pennington and Preston Miller) and Arthur Booth, a former board member and an outspoken critic of Hutton. There were also other physicians who were intensely interested because they were big admitters of patients to the hospital. The conclusion was to strike down the plan of reorganization and request increased physician representation (Bill Collins said it should be 50-50) on the board.

Hutton was generally reluctant to having physicians on the board, and specifically opposed any increase in number. At the board meeting, Stone gave a reasoned and (according to one member) moving presentation in behalf of increased physician involvement. According to Bill Deyo, the current chairman, a potential impasse was broken when board member Sidney Kirschner spoke up and said he could see no problem with having a more equal representation of physicians on the board. Coming from him, Deyo says, such a declaration strongly influenced the other trustees.

Finally, at the insistence of the medical leaders, the number of physicians on the revised, thirteen-member board was increased from four to six, and Hutton's added powers were cut back.

Thus restructuring was completed, not tidily but solidly, with everyone's official approval.

In trying to meet the third assigned task — repositioning the hospital to meet the future — Hutton now says, "That's where it all fell apart."

If one defines an "optimist" as "someone who thinks the future is uncertain," Hutton was just the opposite when he came in 1988, guided by his already-fixed vision* of the future of medical care in this country:

"Managed competition will be the ultimate heart of upcoming drastic changes and reforms in medical care delivery. Managed competition is the model we will get to because it corrects the basic flaw in the existing system — it will take the incentive for finding sick people out of it. Managed care is nothing more than a rock in the stream that leads us across the stream to reform. Reform is going to mean that health care will be organized much more directly. It will not be a free market anymore, and it means that fee for service medicine in time will be out the window. The

---

*Hutton's directed his administrative staff with this overview, but he never did present or discuss this vision of the future with the medical staff as a whole or with its executive committee, although he said he had with a few members individually. This lack of direct communication and open airing and sharing of the views which shaped and drove his policies (although they and the messenger were certain to have been unpopular) may be one reason for the widespread feeling among the physicians that Hutton always had his own personal agenda.

practice of medicine, which is 'too much of a cottage industry,' will increasingly be superceded by mega-organizations which will provide all sorts of services (inpatient surgery, outpatient surgery, other physicians' services, physical therapy services, pharmacy services, home nursing services) and one-stop shopping, a totally integrated system. The system will depend less and less on what happens in hospitals, which is a shrinking market."

In 1993, he has not changed his views, which coincide with those of the Clinton administration. In 1992, for the first time, health care reform became a major issue in our national elections.

In 1988 the concept of "managed competition" was not new. In the 1970s Alain C. Enthoven, a professor of economics at Stanford, began formulating ideas which eventually appeared in an article in the 1986 "Health Care Financing" supplement under the title, "Managed Competition in Health and the Unfinished Agenda." Two of its principal advocates have been Enthoven and Dr. Paul M. Ellwood, a pediatric neurologist from Minnesota, who is widely regarded as the father of HMOs (health maintenance organizations). Informal meetings at Dr. Ellwood's home in Jackson Hole, Wyoming, have taken place for 20 years, but they and the concept received little attention until soaring medical costs forced policy makers on the state and national level to seriously consider change. The concept was set forth in a formal document in 1991.

Hutton predicts that many of the initiatives he began will be accomplished in five years; he said he was guilty only of trying to complete them in 12 to 18 months. He admits that where he went wrong was that he personally (as did some of the board members, he said) became convinced that health care reform was coming down the pike much faster than anticipated, and that he and his team moved too fast in trying to make the transition, getting ahead of most of the medical staff.

His face-saving spin was a good try, but unconvincing. It was not so much his shift of Northside's involvement in managed care into high gear that the medical staff objected to. It was Don Hutton himself who turned them off. It would serve no healthy purpose to detail the litany of complaints (perceived personal discourtesies, misrepresentations and flaws in character) by staff leaders and some others who came to know him well. The point is that their negative feelings towards Don became habitual, deep rooted and sometimes very bitter, at times affecting their objectivity in evaluating the merits of whatever he proposed or accomplished. And just as in a bad marriage, Hutton did not bring out the best in some of the doctors either. The incompatibility which undermined their working relationship was aggravated by but only incidentally related to managed care. In essence, they knew as well as Hutton that the brave new world of national health reform could be coming fast; but they had no confidence in Hutton's leading Northside into it, since they were convinced he was not looking out for their best interest nor, ultimately, the hospital's either. Their perception became their reality.

Since managed care and other projected changes would cut physician incomes, Hutton automatically attributed most of rising physician resistance to pains in the pocketbook. This was undoubtedly a factor but hardly the only one. He had neither the inclination nor the temperament to be a consensus builder. Of the many projects he started, some were promoted without his having made a convincing case or having garnered support from the physicians who were expected to provide the service and/or formally approve his moves.

Under "Blue Indigo," for example, OB care for indigent teenagers would be provided by Northside, but approval by the obstetricians who would be obliged to provide this service was not obtained, and the extent of obligations of this service was not defined, before the proposal went forward.*

*This was a noble and practical idea which Hutton encouraged, but did not handle well when it came to physician involvement. Locally, it has since evolved into a pilot study to (1) create access to the health care system for a limited number of pregnant indigent teenagers in north Fulton County attending an alternative high school, and (2) demonstrate quantitatively the benefits of prenatal care in lowering infant morbidity and mortality. This was in response to the disturbing fact that Georgia now has almost the highest infant mortality of any state. The intent is to create a model of access and care which could be used effectively elsewhere in Georgia.

In 1993, the Northside Foundation provided $50,000 in start-up funds and the program, a.k.a the Atlanta Perinatal Access Program, is now under way. Three physicians, all from Northside, now serve on Blue Indigo's 11-member Atlanta board: Alan Joffe, physician-at-large, the most active physician member; Dwana Bush, family practitioner; and John Lee, neurologist. Don Hutton, now a health care consultant and no longer at Northside, has remained on the Blue Indigo board.

Jack Spanier then chairman of the board, who liked and respected much about Hutton and still does, puts it this way: "He was a square peg in a round hole, his talents more suitable as an entrepreneur than an administrator. And he just didn't have the ability to gain consensus of his primary customer, which is not the patient, but the doctor." In 1992 physicians still had the option of taking their patients, those who were not bound by the restrictions of a managed care contract, elsewhere, such as increasingly attractive St. Joseph's, where some felt they and their patients would be made to feel more at home. Hutton might be able to keep the financial sheet respectable, with the aid of volume-driven managed care connections, Kaiser doctors, an influx of new physicians in the area, and a flurry of outpatient projects and marketing ploys, but a critical element was missing: the physicians' trust in Don Hutton.

Why he did not devote more effort to court the medical staff when he came to Northside in 1988 is conjectural. After all, he had significant difficulties with physicians at Cabell in West Virginia (as it was learned later). Also he was undoubtedly aware, as one of his favorite magazines, *Modern Healthcare* (Special Report, May 27, 1988) reported, that "friction among medical staffs, trustees and management has reached an all-time high ... and the high rate of CEO turnover at hospitals has the industry scrambling to figure out why." In that issue, hospital governing board chairmen rated the value of the CEO's personal characteristics and ability more important than their broad management experience. The two highest rated personal characteristics were commitment to high quality health care and the CEO's reputation and integrity. Persuasiveness with the medical staff also ranked high.

Hutton did cultivate several individual physicians and board members whom he regarded as key or important, and some of those have remained sympathetic with him. But even during his first year at Northside, physicians began finding it difficult to have productive discussions with this very self-assured

CEO or to rely on his assertions. (In contrast with Chris Clark, there was one useful change: Although Clark almost always seemed agreeable, things did not necessarily work out the way one understood they were supposed to; if Hutton disagreed, he usually let one know where he stood, in clear terms.) As time went by, they wound up on opposite sides of the fence on a wide range of issues.

A good illustration was the failure of the medical staff to approve Hutton's selection of a medical director (a.k.a. vice president of medical affairs), a newly created position. Hutton felt the rejection was symptomatic — that the very large medical staff was not only becoming unmanageable, but that its leaders liked it that way. "Those in control could see that having that person (his choice) would destroy their ability to keep it diffuse," and he cited the need for the medical staff to closely control itself as a necessary factor in Northside's future. While the medical staff acknowledged Hutton's need to have someone he could deal with directly instead of having to constantly confront the medical staff, his propensity to "have his own man" was another matter. They wanted to make sure that the position of medical director could not be used as a device for the administration and the hospital to control or by-pass the medical staff.

In the dictionary the first definition of "customer" is "one who purchases goods from another; a buyer; a patron." In that sense, the CEO was right when he said that the payer (including the patient) was the primary customer. His often-repeated declaration, which annoyed some physicians, seemed to serve no purpose other than an explanation for his not getting along well with the medical staff. In the dictionary there is also a second, informal definition of "customer," which Hutton ignored — "a person one has to deal with." He never appeared to accept what is a fact of life: under our present health care system, the administrator still has to deal openly with the medical staff, because "when mama ain't happy, ain't nobody happy." Now, in the larger and more realistic sense, the payer and the physician are both the primary customer.*

---

*In 1991 Rufus Kervin participated in a number of focused interviews involving 50 patients who had been at Northside and other Atlanta hospitals. "The one central thought that came through very clearly from all these patients was that the one dominant factor which brought them to Northside was the quality of the medical staff."

▼▼▼▼

Hutton regards another accomplishment, moving the hospital to take a site and establish a presence in Alpharetta, as the one he believes will remain his thumbprint on Northside. Providing health and physician services directly in that community, he believes, will distinguish the position of Northside for the next thirty or forty years. Its outpatient Cancer Treatment Center (operated by Atlanta Oncology Associates under Dale McCord, in a joint venture with the hospital) was first to arrive in 1992.

It would have shown more foresight for Northside to have opened a satellite hospital in Roswell/Alpharetta long ago, but few could fault Hutton's push to have Northside physicians provide outpatient medical and surgical services there now. An application to build a 125-bed hospital on its beautiful 38 acres at Preston Ridge was turned down in 1991, and no one can predict when it will become a must. (The Alpharetta area is projected to have more than 300,000 residents by 1997.)

▼▼▼▼

Presidents, governors and administrators always get credit for the good things that took place during their term. These occurred during Hutton's time:

A substantial overall increase in oncology services (part of which were due to outside referrals and to the aging of Northside's patient population), including the arrival of an Autologous Bone Marrow Transplant Service. Completion of a second (now 10-story) medical office building, the 980 Doctors Centre, connected to the hospital by a tunnel beneath the street. The ScreenAtlanta program, part of the Institute for Cancer Control, came of age. Begun in Clark's last year, its travelling van became a familiar sight in metro Atlanta, offering low-cost mammography and other cancer and non-cancer (diabetes, lung function, hypertension, cholesterol) screenings, instruction and information.

In 1990, with heavy backing by both the OB department and Hutton, an elegant perinatology service was developed by Larry Stone, a Northside radiologist skilled in OB, prenatal and neonatal ultrasound, in association with Jeff Korotkin, an obstetrician at Piedmont who also had a special interest and experience in dealing with problems in the perinatal period of pregnancy. This addition to Northside's popular OB services, now 25th largest in the nation, was state-of-the-art and highly personalized.

Plans for a Women's Center on campus were completed and a CON for a Cardiac Catheterization Lab was approved. A Director of Medical Education, David Marler, Ph.D., began coordinating joint programs for Northside and St. Joseph's. The impetus for this joint move came from Bill Foley, CEO at St. Joseph's. John McCoy's Ethics Committee, which involved all three hospitals, as well as clergy, psychiatrists, and a variety of other physicians, nurses and other health care workers, offered a valuable new resource and dimension.

And as in other progressive hospitals around the country at that time, Total Quality Management (the "corporate manifesto") and Focused Patient Care were highly touted as working paradigms, and were "in" as buzzwords.

▼▼▼▼

When Hutton came to Northside in 1988, Rufus Kervin reflects, "He was a visionary who made a conscious effort to take a somewhat different approach — meaning that an exceptionally large number of new projects and programs would be started (the community would be involved in many outreach programs), and a concerted effort would be made to expand the hospital and its services in bringing it into an increasingly competitive mode with other health care providers in the community."

As one small example, Kervin was named by Hutton to manage a trial NewVisions program, which, during the period of January 16 - March 27, 1989, rewarded with catalogue-illustrated prizes to employees, auxiliary members, and even physicians (if they were interested) ideas which would reduce hospital costs, increase revenues or save time and effort. Kervin thought that the returns to the employees and the hospital proved more than financial. It gave the employees a sense of active participation and some personal accountability for actions in major parts of the hospital operation.

Then something palpably changed.

Whatever the reason, Kervin observed, "During 1989, 1990 and perhaps 1991, we again lost focus of what our goal and objective really was at Northside. We got involved in a number of projects that stretched our commitment and our ability to keep focused on providing high quality medical and patient care at relatively low cost in our core business area." Medical Staff Chief Larry Stone echoed, "There were lots of Blue Indigos, scattering the hospital's financial resources and its energies, which were needed elsewhere." Hutton, who had initially been steering Northside's ship by the stars, now seemed to be steering more by the lights of the passing ships.

Relations with multiple segments of the strong-willed medical staff drifted downward.* Hutton squabbled with the urologists over owning or leasing the lithotripsy equipment. The hospital and the urologists each wound up with their own. Proposals to enhance physician practices (including a preferred provider list compiled by the administration in response to a request by a major Atlanta company) were interpreted by a number on the medical staff as an attack on its egalitarian nature. (Some said this self-characterization had become a myth.) Proposed or actual preferential treatment, "sweetheart deals," of some physicians favored by administration because they enhanced the reputation of Northside Hospital was viewed as demeaning, unprofessional, and divisive.

In-house physicians were pressured to agree to new contracts and they were provoked once again by Hutton's view, similar to Clark's, that they should not be on the board because of an inherent conflict of interest. Hutton unilaterally cancelled a scheduled equipment committee meeting because its chairman (and hospital board member) also happened to be head of a hospital-based department. James Wellman, Northside's pulmonologist since 1976, felt compelled to leave his hospital-based practice in 1990 following an unfortunate dispute with administration over plans to expand the very successful sleep disorders medicine service which he had initiated.** (Both he and Malaney have had subsequent regrets about the matter.)

Many nurses were also unhappy. They felt taken for granted and were upset by arbitrary staffing cuts and limitations made by management to meet the latter's budget requirements. (Some sections, like OB, fared better than others). They felt the higher levels of management had no real understanding of what skilled nursing was all about and that, in the latter's eyes, nursing care was interpreted as numbers on a piece of paper. As a whole, they did not voice their concerns to management because they were accustomed to being loyal soldiers and, warranted or not, because they feared reprisals. Of the relation of the highest echelon of management with nursing, Malaney says, "I don't think there was any relationship. That was the problem."

When the new COO arrived, Hutton told him, "You're going to make all the decisions for the V.P. of Nursing." This didn't work out and was subsequently changed. "One reason Don didn't get involved with the nurses a lot was that he didn't want to muck up relationships any more than they were already mucked up. When the V.P of Nursing was given full responsibility and authority, this was translated into the conclusion that we didn't give a rap about nursing."

Sources of nurse discontent were similar to those around the rest of the country. Nurse Ellen Evans, in charge of the Medical 5th floor, elucidated some of these: "The job stress of bedside nurses has increased as patients are being admitted with increasing severity of illness and shorter patient stays have created an intensified workload. As patients have become more consumer-oriented, they place more demands on nurses for perfection and attention. The front line nurses are forced by parents and families to address and resolve issues related to other departments, such as an incorrect dietary tray or an overflowing trash can.

"To many nurses, the time clock symbolizes 'blue collar' labor, not professionalism. Since many nurses desire pay for overtime, however, a dilemma

---

*Sensitive to this deteriorating relationship and its potential consequences, Board Chairman Spanier says he tried to bridge the gap. (He had become chairman when Ellen Acquaviva, the previous head, left the board during her term for personal reasons.) Inclined by nature to avoid conflict and confrontation, he made a deliberate attempt to openly back Hutton whenever it seemed appropriate and reasonable. He tried to shore up Hutton with frequent meetings and talks, he recounts, making him understand the consequences of what he was doing or about to do, "but I was never able to change his personality." Spanier learned how uncomfortable and lonely it can be for a full-time practicing physician to be chairman of a modern hospital board when the CEO is at odds with the medical staff.

**In 1983 his laboratory at Northside was the first nationally certified Sleep Disorders Center in Georgia. Wellman now practices on nearby Peachtree Dunwoody Road in an office with pulmonary medicine associates Ron Ovetsky and Dan Callahan and clinical psychologist Alan Lankford, co-director of the Sleep Disorders Center. Their clinic is the largest sleep disorders practice in the state, with eight satellite locations associated with their sleep program. Northside is still their primary admitting hospital and Wellman is now secretary of the medical staff.

exists; if there was no time clock, how could there be overtime? The 'calling off' of nurses, when the inpatient census drops, is understandable, but this decreases nurses' self-esteem when non-nursing departments do not staff their departments based on census and are not subject to 'call-off.' With bed census dropping around the country, nurses face the possibility of more frequent layoffs.

"Non-nursing personnel such as management engineering and decision support are viewed as having more power with determining the delivery of nursing care than are the expert nurses at the bedside. Thus, interpersonal conflict and feelings of inferiority and lack of power to change things exist."

〰️

Hutton says his biggest disappointment was the failure to obtain a Trauma Center at Northside. He is both impassioned and bitter about this. In his view, Northside proclaimed itself the community hospital of North Atlanta from the start and has proven to be that in every other way. He felt "the failure of the medical staff to accept this obligation was (and is) a terrible black mark as well as an embarrassment."* He lay the blame on key individuals in the medical staff who, he said, were busy and did not want to be saddled with the demands of this responsibility (such as obligatory availability and interruptions in their office and hospital work schedule) and the likely associated loss of income.

The physician argument was that a first-rate Level II trauma center required the long-range commitment of large financial resources and a sufficiently large number and an appropriate mix of dedicated physician specialists, nurses and other human resources which, realistically, Northside was not yet prepared to do, since it would more likely be a drain rather than a source of income for the hospital. Physicians questioned his numbers and his projections.

Hutton and his management stood firm, but so did the medical staff (even though Earl Pennington, the even-handed chairman of the medical staff, supported the proposal),** and the board once more rejected the trauma center. In the days of Chris Clark, when the proposed Trauma Center also failed to win sufficient physician support, there were fewer qualified physicians to draw from, but the situation was otherwise unchanged.

Questions mounted about Hutton's business acumen and fiduciary responsibility, squandering or not making the best use of resources. Acting on his own, without prior approval, he made problematic deals and large financial commitments on behalf of the hospital.*** Expensive consultants were hired at every turn.

Steadily deteriorating relationships between Hutton and medical staff officers came to a sudden showdown in October 1992, during the visit of Inovations Associates, a man/woman team of O.D. (Organizational Development) consultants (one physician termed them "industrial psychologists") from a firm in Boston. Hired by administration, the consultants seemed to act as marriage counselors. They had several meetings with the medical staff officers concerning their grievances and with lay members of the board, including discussion of future plans. At a

*Malaney expresses surprise at the intensity of his boss' response and the degree of importance he attached to a trauma center, although he believes the matter will likely come up again.

**He now feels the medical staff probably made the right decision. Actually, Pennington points out, Hutton had his chance and blew it. The trauma network had suggested that the hospital become a Level III Trauma Center, one step below Level II, when the physicians concluded they did not have sufficient manpower to meet the higher designation. Pennington says he personally presented the case for this to the surgical section and won their approval; all that was necessary to make it a reality was for Hutton's own staff to fill out the application and for him to sign it. Six months passed by and the application was never filled out. Then, after Pennington inquired about its status, Hutton went into action, but by this time disenchantment with Hutton by members of the surgical section had grown to the point that the majority were no longer willing to give their approval to the trauma center or to much else he proposed.

***An approved CON for construction of a new outpatient facility is required by the state; the latter limits the number of CONs, but is willing to allow transfer of one to a new owner. In order to obtain a CON for an out-patient surgical center (which will be housed in Northside's new multi-specialty North Fulton Medical Building in Alpharetta), an egregiously large sum of money was used to purchase the CON of an abortion clinic on Peachtree Dunwoody Road, torn down to make room for the MARTA station. Part of the deal was the additionally required ten-year lease of an undesirable, empty, old medical building on Carpenter Drive. Whether this transaction was worthwhile, only time will tell.

In another questioned business arrangement, the private developers of the medical building in Alpharetta were guaranteed they would not lose any money. In another instance, staff time was expended in exploring the feasibility of purchasing other hospitals, although the likelihood of any action was remote.

summation joint conference, also attended by members of the board and management, the last of 30 slides projected on the overhead screen asked, "Would the medical staff be willing to go ahead with the same players?"

The Inovations moderator turned to the new chief of the medical staff, who sat across the table from the CEO. "Well, Dr. Bowen?" To everyone's surprise, including his own, Ed Bowen slapped his hand hard on the table and boomed, "Absolutely not! We have had all we can stand."

This triggered an acute unraveling process which revealed the bulk of the medical staff had unambiguously similar sentiments (a unanimous formal vote of "no confidence" was recorded two days later at a medical planning retreat at the Ritz Carlton, previously scheduled), and the CEO was fired.

There was a golden lining in Hutton's future, in the form of a parachute. This had already been agreed to by board members in negotiations months before. That any hospital administrator, especially one in a non-profit institution, and whose performance was in dispute, would be granted a huge severance payout was a concept alien to most of the physicians, and some recorded their objection.

This situation was one more reminder of how the world had changed and how much our attitudes are a reflection of the times; in this case, how much corporate business concepts and approaches have infiltrated medical care. In the high-level business reasoning of the '80s and '90s, this hospital administrator was the chief executive of a corporation with revenues over a quarter of a billion dollars a year, engaged in a highly competitive business, in which the average "life expectancy" (term of office) of this kind of CEO currently is no more than three to five years, and with multiple clients and audiences to satisfy.

Recognizing there was as much pressure on him as on a coach of a major athletic team, it may not be surprising that several lay members of the board (some of whom were also corporate executives and familiar with golden parachutes) did not think it unreasonable that Hutton or any other qualified CEO in a similar position should be protected by one, too.

If Hutton has been accused of viewing medical care like a corporate businessman, it should be acknowledged that some of the most astute members of the medical staff have become afflicted with the same virus.

Don Hutton

In summary, Donald Hutton was a special breed, a self-styled turn-around expert, who accomplished at Northside basically what he set out to do, with consequences he did not intend.

That he alienated the medical staff in the process is not surprising, since the necessary characteristics of successful change agents differ from those of top management:

Because they feel they have to be aggressive, willing and able to make tough choices and unpopular decisions, always pushing to keep the process moving, change agents may take high risks in the effort and are likely to antagonize part of their clients along the way. By nature and temperament they are usually short-termers. They are also classically outsiders, either outside consultants, or, as in Hutton's case, physically (and perhaps psychologically) outside. A high need for achievement, vision, self-confidence, persistence, empowerment of others and special technical skills complete the profile.

Hutton fit this pattern well. In fact, some say this outsider got stuck in the change agent mode and could not convert to the characteristics of the long-term type of CEO needed to run Northside.

The crowning irony is that, whatever his faults, Hutton's efforts may have paved the way for his successor to have an opportunity to do what he never could: (1) reunify the Northside team, (2) help bring Northside and St. Joseph's close together, and (3) apply the approach of a medically enlightened, successful major business executive to hospital management (albeit in an uncertain period of national health care reform).

COMING TO TERMS WITH MANAGED CARE

Managed Care: A) Plans offered to employers and insurance companies by organizations of providers of health care to cut costs, often by limiting worker options or freedom to choose. B) A general term for organizing networks of doctors and hospitals in order to give people access to more cost-effective health care.

Managed Competition: A model blueprint for health care reform endorsed by the White House. This would organize consumers and employers into large purchasing cooperatives (called "health alliances" or "health insurance purchasing alliances," a.k.a. "hip-icks") that would buy services from partnerships of doctors, hospitals and insurers. Competition based on quality and price would be overseen by a national health board establishing standards for benefit plans. As for the uninsured, contributions from employers and government would allow them to join a cooperative.

HMO (Health Maintenance Organization): Prepaid health plans that provide a range of services in return for fixed monthly premiums. HMOs can be sponsored by a variety of organizations, including the government, hospitals, insurance companies, employers, labor unions and medical schools. HMOs were the earliest form of managed care. "Staff model" HMOs hire their own doctors, who usually practice under one roof.

PPO (Preferred Provider Organization): A network of doctors and hospitals offering incentives (now discounts on their services are a standard feature) for patients to use it. Patients can go outside the network, but must pay more.

POS (Point-of-Service Plan): A tighter modification of a PPO, with a primary-care physician as gatekeeper to guide a patient's care within a specific network of providers. Patients have financial incentive to use the network; they can go outside it, but they must pay more.

IPA (Independent Practice Association): A group of doctors who agree to jointly market their services with managed care providers, typically HMOs. They are free to contract with more than one HMO at a time, as well as see fee-for-service patients. IPA physicians see patients in their own offices.

Capitation: A managed care plan that pays a doctor or a hospital a fixed amount to care for a patient for a given period. Health care providers get paid even if the patient never uses the services; but they don't get extra, even if the costs of care exceeds that amount.

MANAGED CARE AT NORTHSIDE

Georgia has been one of the most militant anti-managed care states, and until the mid-'80s, the provider community was quite content since there was no shortage of patients.

Northside's first association with managed care was in 1984, when it became a charter member of SouthCare Medical Alliance, along with seven other hospitals and medical staffs in the Atlanta area (Piedmont, Kennestone, DeKalb, Gwinnett [including Joan Glancey and Duluth], Cobb, South Fulton and Clayton General [now Southern Regional]). SouthCare is now the largest PPO in Atlanta. Last year it began offering the POS feature. Northside physician Gwynne Brunt is now chairman of its board.

Locally, PPOs cover more people than HMOs but the latter are the big players in terms of hospital admissions and patient revenues. The biggest HMO in Atlanta and Georgia is Kaiser Permanente. It pioneered the HMO concept in California in the 1930s and came to Atlanta in 1985, the year it began association with Northside. (Other earlier HMOs had put roots down in the Atlanta metro area by 1980 but ran into serious financial and organizational snags at that time.) In Atlanta, Kaiser has been under the leadership of J. Harper Gaston, a 1955 graduate of Emory's School of Medicine, until his retirement this year. Richard G. Barnaby in now the V.P. regional manager for Kaiser Foundation Health Plans of Georgia, Inc., and Dr. Richard Rodriguez is the medical director of the Southeast Permanente Medical Group of Georgia, Inc.

Northside and Georgia Baptist are the two hospitals used in Atlanta by Kaiser, which now employs 140 physicians full-time and 58 part-time (regular part-time plus "PRN" as needed). 103 of the Kaiser doctors are on the staff at Northside. About 50% of its hospitalized patients are admitted to Northside. This figure rises to 60% for obstetrical patients, which account for about 2,000 of the 8,300 deliveries this past year. During the past 12 months, 13% of Northside's total revenues have come from Kaiser referrals.

To assure the hospital would not be inundated by managed care patients, in 1990 Northside set an arbitrary limit of 15% of hospital admissions of managed care patients from all sources (including Prudential, Aetna, etc.) and a maximum of 12% from any single source (i.e., Kaiser). In 1991 the figure was not strictly adhered to and blew past 20%. During the past year, as the bed census dropped (in Atlanta and around the country), the arbitrary maximum was discontinued, and this year finds 38% of Northside's hospitalized patients come from managed care sources.

Analyst John Harkey estimates slightly over 50% of metro Atlantans under 65 are now in managed care plans. The rising costs of medical care for employers has been the principal factor, but the increase in number of physicians and the recession have contributed to the recent impetus in the utilization of managed care in Atlanta.

Thanks to Ralph Dunagin, Orlando, Florida.

19

A New Era: The Genial, Fortune 500 Administrator

Sometimes you get lucky.

At the fateful Inovations meeting in October, immediately after the explosive declaration by the chairman of the medical staff, Larry Stone's gaze was drawn to the expression on the face of Sidney Kirschner. This was the very astute, esteemed Kirschner's eighth year on Northside's board, the longest tenure of any current lay trustee, and (he agreed later) he was shocked at the depth of discomfort of the medical staff with the CEO, as expressed by Bowen.

Stone, the savvy ex-chairman of the medical staff, had worked closely with Kirschner and knew him well, and he thought he saw something else in Kirschner's face and manner — the realization that he may have been witnessing the end of an era, that he was already thinking about how to proceed, and his deep personal concern for Northside.

(Kirschner was thinking that Bowen's response, if it indeed reflected the feelings of the whole medical staff, meant the board had no choice but to make a change in administration immediately. And that, if such a conclusion was reached unanimously by the trustees, he felt they had to act with speed, but always like trustees. And they did. They proceeded in orderly, deliberate fashion, though time was pressing. They even independently tested some of Bowen's statements with physicians of many years' association with the hospital, and they found his assessment accurate.)

Stone knew that the 57-year-old Kirschner had recently retired after five years as president and CEO of National Service Industries, a perennially success-

Sidney Kirschner

ful, home-grown, Atlanta-based conglomerate, but his nature was such that he would not stay retired very long. He was healthy (though he had had by-pass surgery), he and his family loved Atlanta, and he was financially independent. Stone had thought, "What if?" and after a current meeting of the board, had made small talk about Kirschner's retirement and casually had asked him if he would consider being a hospital CEO. Kirschner had smiled and said, "That might be interesting," and dropped the subject.*

Stone had mentioned the fanciful idea to Jack Spanier, the board chairman, and probably others, but

---

*On the way to their cars, after the emotional finish of the Inovations meeting, Bill Deyo, the chairman-elect of the board, slapped Kirschner on the back and said, in jest, "How would you like to be a hospital CEO?"

it was not pursued. That is, not until the board made the decision that a change was necessary. Then, all at once, Kirschner began receiving several key calls. Kirschner says he is not sure who broached it first, but the message was the same. They wanted a different kind of administrator and suggested, "Now that you're unemployed, Sid, why not you?"

Indeed, why not? His wife and son pointed out to him that he was more deeply interested in Northside than he realized. They reminded him that many times he had come back from Northside board meetings saying, "Why am I doing this?" but he always stayed with it and obviously cared. Once he began seriously considering it, the opportunity at Northside became very attractive. For him, it satisfied a lot of needs. It had a community content; during his long-time connection with Northside he had seen the hospital grow up as he grew, since he had lived in north Atlanta for two decades, and he knew many of the physicians for a variety of reasons. The board and a portion of the medical staff had known him and worked with him for several years and knew how he operated, so there would not be the normal discomfort that comes with hiring a stranger.

His abilities (and reputation) as an excellent manager and businessman,* including 19 years as an NSI executive, were strong qualifications in the rapidly changing and unstable period of health care reform. As Spanier put it, "It may be very healthy not to have a professional hospital administrator in the job."

Kirschner had already decided that he wanted to do something different before he got too old; "Once this opportunity arose, it felt right." He did not have long to think about it. Hutton resigned during the week following the Saturday denouement at the Ritz Carlton, as it became clear to everyone that his position was no longer tenable.

Kirschner took the plunge. On the next Sunday, November 1, he formally accepted the position of president and CEO. Now, eight months later (June 1993), he is confident he made the right choice.

His taking the helm at Northside had an immediate, profoundly positive impact. The physicians were delighted. They knew him, they liked and respected him and, most important, they trusted him. And the feeling was genuinely mutual. He really cared; he had no personal agenda, no heights to aspire to, no axes to grind. Gone was the adversarial climate. They all — the administrator, the trustees and the medical staff — were partners again, but, this time, with more appreciation of each other's problems than they ever had before.

Trust, accessibility, openness, teamwork, mutual accountability — in a sense, the qualities characterizing Northside's new administrative leadership had come full circle, back to the ambience of the late '60s and early '70s.

These medical staff feelings about Kirschner were shared, but perhaps not as deeply, by the hospital employees, since most did not know him personally, and they had heard these songs before from his predecessors. But from the very beginning everyone found him consistently fair, and his demeanor, equanimity and thoughtful approach induced a much-needed calming, healing effect in a difficult time. He was off to a more than a good start, and the board was happy.

As a seasoned business-world CEO, Kirschner's management style is much nearer to the style of Chris Clark (but without the excesses) than to the one of Don Hutton. He strongly believes the top person should be both visible and accessible, and, except in special circumstances, his place is in the hospital.

When Kirschner took over, he made a concerted effort not to alter the staff he had inherited from Hutton. Although some advised he clean house, just as Hutton had done before him, Kirschner felt it was important, whenever possible, to rebuild confidence in the administration and the hospital without

---

*Canadian-born and raised in New York, he had finished school in New Mexico as a mining engineer, at the time when the aerospace industry began and Russia launched its Sputnik satellite. The emerging aerospace industry offered more opportunities, and he went to work for a small rocket company in Los Angeles in 1956. Looking back, he says, "I've always tended to get involved with emerging situations, where I was able to grow professionally and managerially. I was never bashful about it — if I couldn't get more responsibilities, I changed jobs and cities (the title and the compensation followed suit). I've always been very lucky; every time I have made a change, it has gone in the right direction."

In California he worked for two different aerospace companies and then moved, with his wife, 9-month old twin daughters and a three-year old son, to New Jersey, shortly after the Kennedy assassination, in an engineering management position. He then progressed to the General Dynamics Corp. in New York, in 1967, where he became president of the Electric Motor Division. In 1973 he came to Atlanta and NSI, where he eventually became its COO, president and CEO and then chairman. Kirschner cites the importance of the mentors who have helped him along the way (he acknowledges his indebtedness to Erwin Zaban at NSI) and likes his own mentor role at Northside.

(l-r) Northside Hospital CEO Sidney Kirschner, Saint Joseph's Hospital CEO William Foley and Scottish Rite Children's Medical Center CEO James Tally.

changing people and without bringing in people one did not know. Describing himself as a questioner who challenges almost everything, he found Hutton's COO (Scott Malaney) and key staff (Quattrocchi, Press, Bacon, etc.) very knowledgeable and competent. Kirschner knew that some of them had been friends of Hutton (and still were), but he was pleased they were not uncomfortable working at their same jobs with him. Paraphrasing his view: As true professionals, they were presumed to be good team players; now they simply had a new coach and mentor. As long as they did their job satisfactorily, as long as they were comfortable with Sid and he with them, as long as they were needed — their jobs were secure. Kirschner did a little reorganization. In contrast with Hutton, who was outside the hospital much of the time and delegated responsibility for running of the hospital in reality to Malaney, Kirschner said he and Malaney

divided their responsibilities and, "Scott has been wonderful about this."

The only real downside resulting from this decision was that many of the nurses* and some of the other employees had complaints during Hutton's tenure which they hoped would be addressed when the new CEO took over; with the same management staff under Kirschner they were not sure whether and when and to what extent their concerns would be met, despite his admirable intentions.

On the whole, Kirschner's decision has been vindicated and loyalty has not become an issue. Morale in his key staff has seemed high, at least until the latter part of this month, when, after eight months as CEO, reevaluating the organization of the senior management of the hospital in relation to his own decision-making process and management style, he concluded he did not need a COO.

---

*One basic issue, often obscured by more immediate concerns, that some nurses keep returning to is echoed by Lisa Bacon, V.P. of Patient Care, in charge of nursing: "We give excellent nursing care, but we have technical nursing care; we need to advance professional nursing practice." Northside now has 1,200 nurses, comprising more than half of the 2,200 hospital employees.

He felt that, in today's environment, the CEOs involvement in operations must intensify, organizational layers must be reduced and the top person must be easily accessible to all employees. It would make his job easier when the chief financial officer, and heads of strategic planning and marketing, patient care and human resources all reported directly to him. Kirschner had nothing but praise personally for Malaney.

While the new CEO continues to learn more about the many facets of the hospital, the hospital has been learning from him how a top-notch business executive, accustomed to consensus building on strategic choices and on how to spend limited resources, operates. The decision-making process is now more orderly and complete. Under Hutton, Bob Quattrocchi had made substantial long-needed improvements in Northside's financial infrastructure and operations, but Hutton sometimes moved too fast to make good use of "Q's" resources.

Hutton to some extent kept board members doing "busy work." Now some meetings have been cut back, and board members come to work. Gradually, in logical steps, Kirschner is working with others at fresh looks in the gamut of the hospital's operations, in order to do them better and not waste time, money or human resources.

When Kirschner visits different sections of the hospital and asks questions, he says, "I don't find this a bashful place at all. I've never worked in an environment with so many intelligent people. In most companies, the organization's structure is more like a pyramid, but here it is a long, horizontal layer. You have physicians, nurses and administration who are all articulate, bright, educated and caring. I've never worked in an industry where the people have so much care about their business."

Northside's popular new leader, with his unassuming, conciliatory touch, helped change the climate on The Hill as a whole overnight. For two decades, efforts to get the two adult hospitals close together had produced only limited results.* Now anything seemed possible.

Kirschner reached out to the CEOs of St. Joseph's (William Foley) and Scottish Rite (James Tally), and they responded. Trust restored, they now have a cordial, cooperative relationship and communicate well with each other. That is fortunate, since both the hospitals and the physicians have come to realize how much they need each other in this uncertain time.

Ten weeks after Kirschner became CEO, the lead article in the *Atlanta Business Chronicle* (by Dean Anason, January 8, 1993) was headlined, "An Urge to Merge? Hospitals on 'The Hill' Consider More Collaboration":

Despite constant strategic maneuverings by medical institutions around Atlanta, probably no other place is the subject of more speculation on "what could be" than the three hospitals on The Hill.

Health care observers have said for years that if Northside Hospital, Saint Joseph's Hospital of Atlanta and Scottish Rite Children's Medical Center combined administrative and clinical operations, no one could stop them. Businesses might start knocking on their doors for employee health coverage contracts.

"They could just overpower anything up there," says Don Logan, CEO of the Southern Regional Medical Center.

Although the hospitals' CEOs respond that they do not plan extensive collaboration soon, such possibilities are "an area ripe for exploration," says James Tally, Scottish Rite's CEO. "We haven't been blind to the fact of what is developing here," Tally says …

Together, the three hospitals assign privileges to more than 1,900 doctors,** employ more than 6,300 employees, and have blue-chip board members from companies such as BellSouth Corp., The Southern Co., Law Companies Inc., Sun Trust and Wachovia and King & Spalding.

If the hospitals were to combine, their gross revenues would make them just shy of Scientific-Atlanta Inc., the city's largest technology products manufacturer.

With a combined 966 licensed beds, the three Northside hospitals would be second only to Grady Memorial Hospital's 1,162 licensed beds. The three hospitals actually have more staffed beds than Grady …

This year, Atlanta has been learning more about The Hill and its concept, and the term is now

---

*In Hutton's era the hospitals did cooperate on traffic planning, security, medical waste management, landscaping, pastoral education and health care forums. A Tri-Hospital task force, which included representatives of the doctor group, MCNA, did come up with a combined employee medical insurance plan, and there was cooperation in dealing with Marta representatives. They also joined in an application process for Hospice of the South. Hutton said that during his years there was no great incentive for the hospitals to really work together, nor for the hospitals and physicians, because they were all doing well on their own.

**This figure is too high because some doctors are on the staff of more than one of the hospitals.

COMPOSITION OF NORTHSIDE HOSPITAL MEDICAL STAFF IN 1993							
	ACTIVE	ASSOCIATE	PROVISIONAL	COURTESY	CONSULTING	HONORARY	TOTAL
FAMILY MEDICINE	11	3	7	16	0	2	39
INTERNAL MEDICINE	113	35	51	76	0	4	279
OB\GYN	80	24	26	20	0	8	158
PEDIATRICS	82	28	19	50	2	3	184
PSYCHIATRY	17	6	7	37	0	2	69
SURGERY	110	36	51	82	3	10	292
ANESTHESIA	17	7	0	0	0	0	24
EMERGENCY MEDICINE	6	3	1	1	0	0	11
PATHOLOGY	7	0	3	1	0	0	11
RADIOLOGY	11	1	3	0	0	0	15
RADIATION THERAPY	1	0	1	2	0	0	4
TOTAL	455	143	169	285	5	29	1086

commonly used. For example, a full-page spread in the *Atlanta Journal/Constitution* on April 11, 1993, by Diane R. Stepp, began: Atlanta's Pill Hill, Ringed by Scottish Rite Children's Medical Center and Northside and St. Joseph's Hospitals, has helped create an Atlanta medical megalopolis:

The Hill, north Fulton's largest employer, is home not only to three hospitals but also 11 major office buildings and high-rise office towers. It anchors the southern tip of the Perimeter Center/Georgia 400 corridor, which claims more overall office space than downtown Atlanta.

With 966 beds and gross revenues of $620 million annually, the tri-hospital complex is uniquely positioned to become a national model for community health care, some experts believe.

(A pictorial guide, along with a synopsis of the medical and other features of The Hill, as of 1992, were included in the article and are reproduced on the following page. The only 1993 change from the synopsis is that the opening of the Glenridge Connector in latter 1992 has helped considerably in relieving the traffic migraine. Opening of the six-lane Georgia 400 Extension tollway, which passes by the hospital, in August of this year, may further ease traffic flow).

Most members of the three medical staffs, which overlap, had been for closer ties all along. Ken Melby, chief of staff at St. Joseph's, and Bronier Costas, president of the medical staff at Scottish Rite, are both also members of Northside's staff. The majority of St. Joseph's physicians are also on Northside's roster, and all the pediatricians who practice at Northside are also on the staff at Scottish Rite. Northside lists 1,086 physicians on it medical staff (57% on the active or provisional staff, an additional 13% in associate category (which lies between active and provisional). St. Joseph's lists 730 on its medical staff (with 57% on the active or provisional staff; it does not have an associate category).

E. Napier (Buck) Burson, the former long-time medical director at St. Joseph's, says, "The future of medicine in this area — The Hill — has unlimited possibilities. We have seen growing cooperation between Northside and St. Joseph's as well as Scottish Rite. I predict that these three facilities will merge in some way — perhaps in the delivery of services. If not, then one institution under one name. Competition has been keen between the institutions' medical services here and has served us well."

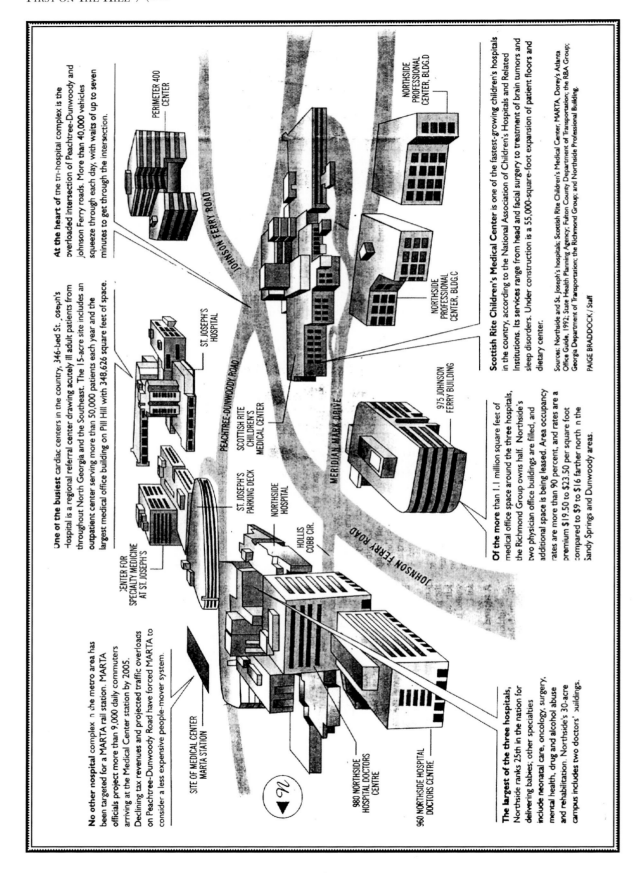

The Hill, 1992

The Medical Center of North Atlanta (MCNA), an organization of a good number of physicians from all three hospitals (and a component of the Tri-Hospital Task Force) had been informing doctors in matters of common interest and doing what it could to promote unity on The Hill since before it was incorporated in 1985. At one time it had about 450 members; now the regulars have dwindled down to about 240. Hutton said the MCNA was an unorganized and ineffective organization because it didn't speak for anyone. He added that was not a reflection on MCNA's durable chairman, Gordon Azar (he praised his ideals, hard work and unstinting commitment) or its other leaders.

It is true that under Azar's patient, plodding, even-tempered guidance, MCNA has not been a union, a political force or a partisan advocacy group, but it was never intended to be. And, if it had no clout, Azar's perception was that Hutton did what he could to assure it would not acquire any.

Azar and the other long-time members regarded it as a catalyst for cooperation, a planning agency, a counselor and an information resource. Non-confrontational, they believed it was a necessary element — a part of the team and organizational infra-structure — ready to be put to use when the hospitals were truly willing to work together.

On December 1, 1992, exactly one month after Kirschner took office, MCNA's perseverance began paying off. After hearing the report of the Managed Care Task Force Committee of the Tri-Hospitals and MCNA, the three CEOs unanimously endorsed the managed care working plan. The plan has two arms: (1) a joint PHO (Physician Hospital Organization), the legal entity for marketing. This would enable contracting for managed care services with employers, insurance companies, etc. And, (2) a second legally registered organization, called the North Georgia Regional Healthcare Network, for joint ventures. The joint venture activity is designed to give the highest efficient cost structure for use under the PHO. It would also, the announcement stated, "enable the expansion of services, provide services more efficiently, improve upon an already high standard of clinical excellence, increase access for patients and physicians and allow a greater focus on community health."

In March 1993, the Task Force selected Wyatt & Company of New York as consultants for a joint PHO feasibility study and tentatively projected that a Tri-hospital PHO could be operational by the first of next year. Although the major thrust since that time has been toward a Tri-hospital PHO,* there is movement also toward an separate, co-existent PHO at each of the hospitals, which have areas of different clinical focus, in order to capitalize on the special features of each hospital and to provide flexibility in the now highly competitive medical marketplace in metro Atlanta.

In April 1993, the two adult hospitals announced the formal structure to work on joint ventures, after it had been ratified by a working group of 28 people, (comprising an equal number of physicians, trustees and administration from both hospitals) and approved by both hospital boards. "The only reason we did it initially with St. Joseph's," Kirschner says, "is that it is easier to work with two people (who had more in common) rather than three. Scottish Rite (complementary, non-competitive, and 'sort of neutral') is an integral part of all our activities." The first principal area of clinical focus, it was agreed, would be to explore the possibility of bringing the oncology service of both hospitals closer together.

~~~~

Eight months after Hutton left, no one blinks at managed care anymore; it is a fact of life. Kirschner says, "Even if you say managed care is your customer, managed care wants a hospital with a fine reputation, they want value and they want appropriate costs. Managed care dictates where the patient goes; they will go to the place that is shaped by the physicians. I have no difficulty saying to the physicians, 'You're customers and partners,' because I really believe they are. How do you achieve any-

*Surgeon Earl Pennington was selected to spearhead Northside's Tri-hospital activity. Kirschner commented, "It is important that a physician lead this activity, because by and large the hospital can make its own decision very quickly. The physician impression of a PHO is that he (she) gives up a degree of independence to join what is basically a collective bargaining organization. One needs a lot of trust and confidence to do those things. It is mandatory that a very respected physician lead this activity, explore alternatives, understand it himself, and be convinced it is the right thing, before he convinces other physicians. Pennington is as able a representative as you can find. This respect has to be carried down to the organization he's from, but he has to be respected by the other hospitals as well."

thing without physicians as partners? If there ever was a time when physicians and the hospital have to work as one with everyone in the hospital, it is now. It's going to become dramatically so."

The wave of the present and near future, everyone connected with health care acknowledges, is more and different strategic alliances* responding to the medical market place, in Atlanta and in larger cities around the country. SouthCare (Atlanta's largest PPO, of which Northside is an important member) is an example of a network of hospitals and preferred providers which offer a better pricing structure in return for guaranteed volume. In 1992 SouthCare also developed a POS (point of service) plan, a hybrid PPO-HMO arrangement featuring deeper discounts and tighter utilization management, with the general internist or the general pediatrician as gatekeeper of access to care. (At present this new wrinkle covers 5,000 lives; the PPO still covers 400,000).

The ballgame keeps changing; at this point no one can predict, with any measure of certainty, what else will evolve and when. Gwynne Brunt, now chairman of the board of SouthCare and chairman-elect of the medical staff, says, "Most likely, PHOs will be an evolutionary step along the road to the vertical integration of health care delivery, in which the physicians become employees of the hospital, the entities form a single foundation or the physicians own the hospital."

Musing about the nearer future, Kirschner says, "Eventually, they (the bulk purchasers of medical care) would come to one body and say, 'This is what I am prepared to pay.' Unfortunately, it is called capitation. From that, it leads to, 'If there only a fixed amount of money, how is it shared?' This has to be resolved with the physicians, and that requires an area of trust."

<hr>

As even the general public now knows, the gatekeeper controlling access to health care under the major types of managed care programs (the HMOs, the POS version of PPOs, etc.) is the primary care physician. Having a sufficient supply of these generalists (the family practitioners, the general internists and general pediatricians),** with a mutually satisfactory working relationship, is essential to the success and the efficiency of the "at risk" managed care plans. Northside, the Tri-Hospital task force and even the MCNA are searching for the best ways to best implement such an arrangement on The Hill.

The certified family practitioners, who are highly in demand, are low in number. Only 11 members of the Family Practice section are listed on the "active staff." According to family practitioner Tom High, not all of these regularly admit patients to Northside, and some who maintain an "active staff" status never admit patients. (The department is infused with doctors from managed care organizations, such as Kaiser, whose primary loyalty is to their own organization, so that the Family Practice section is not a cohesive group.)

---

*Noting that employers are demanding providers that are accessible to employees across the metro area and can handle a large volume of patients in various services, John Eudes, director of corporate development at the Emory University System of Health Care, points out (in the *Atlanta Business Chronicle* Jan. 8, 1993) that "No institution in and of itself can be all-encompassing." As a consequence, he says, hospitals will probably be participating in multiple agreements that will vary from employer to employer and service to service. "In some way, shape or form, you'll end up collaborating with everyone in the marketplace. The competition concept isn't black and white anymore. It's real grey."

**Only one-third of the physicians in this country are now primary care physicians, compared to 30 years ago, when the ratio to specialists was 50-50, and when it was estimated that 43% of physicians were general practitioners. About 1970, the year Northside opened, the American Board of Family Practice was established and the vanishing "general practitioner" was replaced by the "family practitioner."

At the time Northside opened, several of the "general practitioners," as they were called, had operating room or delivery privileges, but gradually they were locked out of this portion of their practice, as the specialists (and their national boards and specialty societies) dictated the qualifications and the standards. According to Omer Eubanks, Northside was the first hospital in Atlanta to establish a separate Family Practice section of the medical staff and the first to establish a separate Family Practice department. During Northside's early years, one of the family practitioners in Roswell, Jim Langford (with his associate, Omer Eubanks), was often the largest individual physician source of patient admissions to the hospital.

Over the years, many of the family practitioners felt increasingly squeezed out and found the reward for using the hospital less than the hassle of making rounds and fulfilling the requirements necessary to maintain privileges. More and more often, the family practitioners referred patients to specialists early and tended to use the hospital less. The effect was to decrease the influence of the family practitioner on the hospital and its operation.

The family practitioners view their new popularity with mixed feelings. On one hand, they feel vindicated to know they will have an important role in any health care system that evolves from healthcare reform; they are glad that they have plenty of work to do and that their average incomes, now at the bottom rung of the medical ladder, are expected to rise.

On the other hand, the nature of their practice, providing continuity of care on a personal basis, may well change. On The Hill, where the overwhelming number of physicians are specialists, the family practitioners see triage and screening occupying a greater part of their time and energy. Like other physicians, they see their professional independence threatened and their autonomy further diminished, as traditional fee-for-service medicine appears on the way out. They are concerned that the PHOs and other managed care organizations will make them an offer they can't refuse.

In the meantime, however, skilled primary care physicians in the northside area are being appreciated more by the public than they have been for many years. The new CEO, for example, can afford the finest of medical care; his own personal physician is a general internist.

<hr/>

"Pursuing every avenue of increasing value," to use Kirschner's phrase, Northside is proceeding with physical modification of two pilot areas, Emergency and Neurosciences. In doing so, it is testing the Patient Focused Care approach to operational and structural reorganization which it adopted under Hutton in February 1992* and has been exploring ever since. Faced with the necessity of cutting costs, improving services, weeding out inefficiencies built into the system in an earlier time and gearing for an increasingly competitive future, most hospitals in this country have begun going down this same path, in one way or another.

"Patient-centered care" is neither a new concept nor a model blueprint. It is simply the name given to a methodical, thorough, realistic way of thinking about or taking a new look at things — at all the components involved in taking care of people in hospitals. This approach uses the people who work within a process to take the process apart; then (in its most idealized, fully developed, prototype form) the system is reassembled and rebuilt into a new system to make it more efficient and accomplish multiple purposes:

(1) to satisfy all the "customers" (i.e. patients, physicians, nurses and other caregivers, and all other employees). The patient would always come first, but the hospital also wanted to create an environment in which all who were there to serve them felt that all their efforts were put to best use — they could work smarter and not harder,

(2) to improve the quality (including consistency) of delivery of services,

(3) to prepare the hospital and its employees to be able to rapidly respond to change (in "customer" needs, changes mandated by or in adjustment to upcoming healthcare reform, and changes responsive to the realigning, competitive medical marketplace), and, hopefully,

(4) directly or indirectly, to decrease operating costs, at least in the long run.

Key PFC features include putting as many services as close to the patient as possible, redesign of work and re-deployment of staff (including cross-training, when feasible), decentralization of services (when practical), restructure of facilities and appropriate automation of time-consuming functions.

The Neurosciences, a newly created section of the hospital on 4 North, appears easier to implement than the ER. The Emergency department is a logical pick for a pilot area at Northside, since operational reorganization, physical restructuring and expansion, and relocation for better visibility and access by patients have been needed for a long time. There are difficulties, however, since it is hard to predict the degree of future utilization of each of the components in the intended expanded scope of the E.R. An enlarged and improved fast-track "Health Express" for care of minor emergencies, with modified cost, is a critical feature. Since plans for construction of a new ER will require CON approval by the state, the application is being submitted this summer.

*At that time Northside was one of only 18 hospitals (out of approximately 7,000 in this country) trying this "new paradigm," adapted from the business management world, according to Hugh Autry. Autry, the well-liked director of this project and former head of respiratory therapy services, has been at Northside almost 20 years. According to him, of the "hundreds" of other hospitals now considering or engaged in implementing this approach, none has thus far used the ER as a pilot area.

Northside Hospital/Alpharetta Campus, 1993

The ER is not only a vital hospital service; it also a vital area financially for most hospitals. In 1992, 22% of all admissions and over 45% of non-obstetrical admissions to Northside were from the ER, and 15% of all patients seen in the ER were admitted to the hospital. A year earlier, the American Hospital Association predicted that during the '90s well over 50% of a hospital's total revenue will derive directly or indirectly from the Emergency department.

One thing the author learned about complex organizational operations a long time ago: the farther one is away from a problem, the easier it is to be confident about a solution. Logical directives from management may not work because (a) they do not take into consideration the special factors that may be obvious only to those who have to deal with the problems directly, or (b) the consequences of altering interactive human relationships cannot always be foreseen.

As one small example, in reference to job flexibility, I recall a time years ago in the Radiology department when we abandoned the few efforts at cross-training although we did accomplish what we set out to do. Cross-training of employees who were technically licensed created a new difficulty. Such technologists became more versatile, and therefore more valuable, and were siphoned off by groups of physicians and by other hospitals/organizations willing to pay them more, which Northside, under its uniform salary structure, was unwilling or unable to do at the time. Moral: In a competitive environment, if hospitals cross-train their employees, they must be prepared to reward them for their increased versatility.

St. Joseph's began exploring patient-centered care in 1991, and also designated two pilot units, which are being reevaluated. Since last year the whole project has been under Bobbie Rhodes, who had worked 12 years in critical care, and small-scale changes have already been proven useful in several areas.* Bobbie Rhodes and Hugh Autry, both earnest, dedicated and very knowledgeable directors of patient-centered care programs at hospitals across the street from each other,

have up to now never even met, except briefly. This serves as a commentary on how things have been done in the past. This, too, will change.

As metro Atlanta mushrooms northward, Northside Hospital/Alpharetta's gorgeous expanse of campus near State Bridge Road, with quick access from the GA 400 expressway, looks better all the time. There the 100,000 square-foot multispecialty medical building, scheduled for completion by this year's end, will also house Northside's new Outpatient Surgical Center, a branch of the Scottish Rite Children's Medical Center and educational activities (women's health services, childbirth classes, etc.). These join the Cancer Treatment Center, including state-of-the-art radiation therapy facilities, which opened last year. It is no wonder that Ted Walker, the capable executive director of the expansion into North Fulton County, feels more at home all the time; he grew up there.

〰〰〰

There is a buoyant mood at Northside these days. There are still major problems to be faced, just as elsewhere on The Hill, just as there will always be. And the pace of change is accelerating, with new and shifting alliances and relationships, as health care moves into unchartered waters. Hospital census continues to drop around the country, Atlanta being no exception, and most hospitals are now "proactively downsizing." It is unlikely that Northside can remain unscathed. But here the tension is gone, the team has a leader they have confidence in and who is trusted by the rest of The Hill. It can't last forever, but the honeymoon with the new CEO continues.

The only concern expressed about him is that he may tire of the relentless pressures from all directions on a hospital administrator in the '90s, that one day he may look around and say, "Who needs all this?"

Sid Kirschner responds, "I recognize that the demands and the complexities are much greater than I ever envisioned, but I pledge that I will stay here as long as the people and the trustees want."

---

*Rhodes says, "Because patient-centered care (PFC) is a way of thinking, and not a process, the key to its success is the preparation and selection of the right people. People have to buy into it and be truly motivated internally; they have to think it both in their heads and their hearts. It conflicts with all the inefficiencies we have built into the system — we can't afford these any longer. The problem, and it is a real one, is selecting the right people for the right fit; the job categories they design may no longer fit the ones who designed them. The fit, in pilot projects particularly, must be very tight. There is no room for error, as you have in the more traditional system."

Closing Reflections

Like the president of our country, what the administrator can ultimately accomplish depends as much or more on his own character, psychological makeup and personality, on the perception of him by his constituents and partners, and on what he is willing to risk fighting for, as it does on the intrinsic merit of the programs and policies he would like to push. It is for this reason I deemed it necessary to spend a seemingly disproportionate amount of time on each administrator and his interaction with his partners, hospital employees and outside forces.

We are all a product of and are inseparable from our times, and each of our four administrators personally characterized and was oriented to a different epoch: Taylor embodied the idealistic, cooperative '60s and early '70s. Clark zeroed in on cutting costs in patient care but also created an expensive bureaucracy of MBAs and other new employees to deal with the increased complexity and number of services accompanying hospital expansions in the '70s and '80s. Hutton was the competitive entrepreneur of the latter '80s, when more and more of the major decisions were made by people who had less and less direct knowledge and experience with patient care, and medicine was viewed more as a commodity and less as a service, thereby becoming more amenable to marketing. And now Kirschner, who, by not being trained as a hospital administrator (instead, qualified by being an experienced CEO of a major business, the first real businessman in the bunch, plus serving eight years as a hospital trustee) symbolizes the unconventional approach, which may be most appropriate for today's fast-changing, cost-driven medical world of shifting allegiances and strategic alliances, waiting for the government to change the ground rules.

Although much about early Northside was unique, time has shown its subsequent history to be a fairly representative slice of the history of hospitals across this country and the forces affecting them during the past 25 or more years. For those interested in health care reform, this narrative of such a microcosm should provide a decent background for understanding or recalling a great deal of where we are coming from.

Time has also proved Northside's founders right in their emphasis that the governing board, administrator and medical staff must all be interdependent working partners. Each has an indispensable role in which it cannot function properly without the loyal support of the other two. There is no real loyalty without a continuity of mutual trust, respect and honesty. These intertwined qualities provide both the glue that binds them together and the oil that eases friction between them. Two of the past administrators, for example, were unwise when they tried to control or manipulate the medical staff, because these moves only bred mistrust. What was surprising was that these two smart people either did not appreciate the magnitude of that predictable consequence or chose to ignore it.

Hospitals have a lot in common with other large organizations — they have structure and hierarchy, chain of command and job descriptions. How they function, in practice, is also similar. Productivity depends heavily on personal motivation, working relationships and interactions and job satisfaction. Mutual respect, honesty and trust — the same critical qualities (the presence or absence of which affects the durability of all human relationships) and issues which have surfaced repeatedly in this narrative — are an indispensable part of job satisfaction. A hospital can expect loyalty from its employees only if they perceive that the hospital can be counted upon to look out for their welfare as its own.

The 1991 increase in number of physicians on the board has given them what they asked for — more direct sharing in the responsibility for Northside's future. This means that they have both the opportunity and obligation of insuring that the laypersons on the board as well as the administrator receive a more complete continuing education on matters affecting the quality and quantity of patient care, as seen from their first-hand perspective, so that a more balanced input into decision-making can be obtained. It also helps insure that the concerns and interests of the physicians will always be taken into consideration in planning and making commitments by the hospital. But the primary loyalty of the physicians who become trustees must always be to the board and to the interests of the hospital — it is not their function to champion the diverse wishes of the large medical staff whose elected leaders have the responsibility of presenting their own case. The distinction may be a fine line but it continues to be a very important one. Like the majority of their fellow citizens, most physicians don't like politics; they like medical politics even less — but the majority must become more actively involved in the process which results in the power to make decisions over their own lives and those of their patients.

It has been a very gratifying experience for me to work with so many dedicated and bright people towards similar goals over such a long period of time. Some have not been so wonderful; some not so bright. Experiencing the spectrum was itself rewarding. I have seen a few greedy physicians — more in current times — but I am proud of the lasting integrity of most of the doctors I have known and worked with at Northside. It is my feeling that there are two small groups of greedy doctors. There are those who would be greedy no matter what their occupation. The other group, I believe, reflects the times they grew up in. They were attracted to entering medical school at a time when physicians' incomes were rising faster than

the rest of the economy, when hospitals and medical services were expanding, when advances in medical technology opened new vistas and new challenges and when the national government encouraged the private corporate ethos in medical care. The practice of medicine became quite appealing on many counts, attracting the brightest and the best, and the expectation of high financial rewards did not hurt. A few of this same small minority of doctors appear to be trying to cash in before the roof of health reform crashes down on their heads.

I am happy to report that many of the older physicians I know, despite their grave concerns about the future uncertainties in medical practice and in patient care, still practice with the same dogged idealism and integrity of their youth. For example, since 1985 Gordon Azar has served as head of the MCNA (Medical Center of North Atlanta), a time-consuming labor of love for which he has received scant appreciation. When I recently reviewed the history and status of MCNA with him, I asked, "Gordon, what do you want out of all this?" His even, earnest reply: "I just want to be remembered as one of the founders of the best medical center in the country."

▬▬

Although many have had a hand in making Northside what it has become, I would like to reiterate my personal appreciation and admiration for the remarkable quality, quantity and duration of efforts of John McCoy and Lea Richmond, who managed, through it all, to maintain their own independent spirit and forthrightness. It is hard to see how anyone could give more of oneself to any institution.

▬▬

The trouble with writing history, the saying goes, is that there is no future in it. And yet the question most often asked me regarding this book is whether I have any predictions.

This narrative ends in late June 1993, before our government has announced its proposals to overhaul our health care system. It does not require a crystal ball to make two safe, general appraisals:

(1) In the short term, national health care reforms will arrive in steps, rather than a one-time drastic change.

This is because arriving at a consensus on several interconnected, controversial and complex issues is not easy. The public is unwilling to risk crippling the system in order to try to make it work better, and public trust in the national government remains low. (Significant fresh initiatives are already taking place from within the health care industry and by several states, primarily in response to escalating costs and to competition.)

(2) No matter what system we wind up with, the people — doctors, nurses and other caregivers — will make it work somehow. They may not like it, and a transitional generation may have wistful longing for the faulted "good old days," but in time they will become adjusted to it. And the following medical generation or the one after that, having personally known no other, will accept it as the way things are and will work with it or around it. Their own bottom line, after all, is not the financial statement but taking care of people's health.

Appendices

APPENDIX ONE
Chronology

1962 March: Northside Hospital Planning Association formed, Dr. John McCoy, chairman.

1963 January: Northside Hospital Association Inc. charter obtained.
May: Board of trustees named; William Wainwright first regular chairman (1963-65).
July: Site recommended by site committee, Dr. Lea Richmond, chairman.

1964 September: Use permit approved by Fulton County commissioners.
November: Board purchased 35-acre site (sold part).

1965: Luke Swensson became chairman of Northside Hospital Association, Inc., planned fund-raising.

1966 April: Hospital Authority formed, Hollis Cobb first chairman.
Fund-raising campaign begun, Swensson in charge.

1967: Matching funds (federal and state) obtained.
June: Fund-raising completed.
Swensson died.
Architects drew plans.

1968 March: Hill-Burton grant.
April: Joe Taylor became administrator.
June: Groundbreaking.
Planning Association formally became Medical Staff.

1970 June 27: Hospital dedication.
Monday, July 5: Hospital opened. Hospital newsletter for internal distribution called The Thing. (Short-lived, later became the Pacemaker.)

1972 August: $7 million mini-expansion, tripling the size of the ER area, expanding maternity services and newborn area. Increased community education programs. Additions to administrative team: Dick Bibel (Fiscal Affairs), George Simpson, Bart Miller. Medical Staff Chairman Bob van de Wetering appointed 3-man committee (John McCoy, Lea Richmond and David Cohen) to coordinate medical care planning between Northside, St. Joseph's and Scottish Rite.

1973: Joe Taylor left and Chris Clark became second administrator.

1975: Completed construction of a four-story, $9 million annex, adding 98 beds and two operating suites. Doubled the size of the Coronary Care Unit and expanded the intensive care unit.

1976: Scottish Rite opened.

1977: Added radiation therapy facilities and department, CT equipment and space for same, a doctors' lounge, a conference room, an enlarged cafeteria with 160 seats, and an area for a.m. patient admissions.

1978: St. Joseph's opened.

1985: Completed a free-standing Child Care Center. Second Doctors' Building (now called Doctors' Centre).

1987: Added two new floors to the patient tower, updated existing floors. Constructed a new, five-story patient tower. Opened a new intensive care wing. Renovated public spaces and ancillary areas. Added MRI in joint venture with St. Joseph's.

1988: Chris Clark left and Don Hutton become third administrator.

1990: Purchased 38 acres in Alpharetta to construct physician office building, outpatient surgery center and outpatient diagnostic services. Primary intent was to construct a 100-plus bed hospital, but this has been turned down thus far by state planning agency.

1992: Outpatient Cancer Treatment Center opened in Alpharetta (Preston Ridge). Don Hutton fired; Sidney Kirschner became fourth administrator.

APPENDIX TWO

LIST OF DOCTORS WHO JOINED THE NORTHSIDE HOSPITAL MEDICAL STAFF 20 OR MORE YEARS AGO

Note: Those who joined the **Provisional** Medical Staff prior to 1968 were not listed as **members** of the Medical Staff until 1968, when they were all formally approved by the newly formed Hospital Authority.

Status column indicates current (1993) status:

* All members in **Active** category have been at Northside 20 years or longer.

* Some now in the **Courtesy** and **Honorary** categories have also been at Northside as long or almost as long. (Almost all in the Honorary category have now retired from practice).

* The names of several former members who are now **deceased** (for example, Earl Hathcock and Charles Rogers, both former Chiefs of the Medical Staff) have been removed from this computer list. Some others were Dan B. Kahle, G.R. Sutterfield, Ralph L. Robinson, Cheney C. Sigman, Jr., William E. Huger, Jr. William Mendenhall, C.A.N. Rankine, Cary Harper, Edna Porth, Edward D. Reisman, Walter Murray and Larry Bregman.

NAME		APPOINT	STATUS	MEDICAL SCHOOL	RESIDENCY
ABEND	MELVIN	07/01/73	ACTIV	TUFTS	BOSTON CITY
ABRAMS	NORMAN	03/01/70	HONRY	UNIVERSITY OF MIAMI	EMORY
ADAIR	HAROLD	04/01/69	ACTIV	TULANE	GRADY
ALARCON	ALFREDO	01/01/72	CRTSY	UNIV OF MEXICO	LDS, SALT LAKE CITY
ALDERMAN	EARL	11/01/68	ACTIV	MEDICAL COLLEGE OF GA	PIEDMONT
ALEXANDER	HAROLD	01/01/72	ACTIV	TUFTS	NEW ENGLAND MED CENT
ALEXANDER	JAMES	11/01/73	ACTIV	MEDICAL COLLEGE OF GA	HENRY FORD HOSPITAL
ALLAN	CHRISTOPHER	07/01/73	ACTIV	UNIV OF MI	MAYO CLINIC
ALPERIN	HERBERT	01/01/73	ACTIV	EMORY UNIVERSITY	KINGS COUNTY, NY
AMATRIAIN	FERNANDO	04/01/69	CRTSY	EMORY UNIVERSITY	GA BAPTIST
ANTROBUS	LEROY	11/01/68	RESIG	TULANE	CRAWFORD LONG
APPEL	SIDNEY D.	09/01/72	CRTSY	MEDICAL COLLEGE, SC	UNIV OF PA
APPLE	DAVID JR.	06/01/70	CRTSY	UNIV OF PA	GRADY
ARNOLD	JOSEPH A.	05/01/70	ACTIV	MEDICAL COLLEGE OF GA	DEKALB GENERAL HOSP
ARONOVITZ	GERSON H.	09/01/71	RESIG	STATE UNIV OF NY	STATE UNIV. OF NY
ASHER	HAROLD	09/01/72	ACTIV	EMORY UNIVERSITY	TULANE, NEW ENGLAND
ASKREN	EDWARD L.	11/01/68	HONRY	U OF ILLINOIS	MINNEAPOLIS GEN HOSP
AVERETT	JAMES B., JR	04/01/69	CRTSY	EMORY UNIVERSITY	PIEDMONT
AVERY	WILLIAM G.	11/01/68	HONRY	EMORY UNIVERSITY	GRADY
AZAR	GORDON J.	04/01/69	ACTIV	EMORY UNIVERSITY	PIEDMONT
BAILEY	M. THOMAS	06/01/70	ACTIV	MEDICAL COLLEGE OF GA	GRADY
BARTHOLOMEW	PHILIP R	04/01/69	ACTIV	MACON HOSP	TALMADGE MEM HOSP
BAYNE	LOUI G.	11/01/68	ACTIV	U OF ARKANSAS	CHARITY HOSP, TULANE
BEAN	JAMES L.	07/01/73	CRTSY	MEDICAL COLLEGE OF GA	MED CTR OF CEN GA
BELCHER	WILLIAM T JR	04/01/69	CRTSY	EMORY UNIVERSITY	GRADY
BERMAN	JEROME D.	11/01/68	HONRY	EMORY UNIVERSITY	GRADY
BERRY	J. NORMAN	11/01/68	ACTIV	DUKE	DUKE
BLACK	PAUL W.	04/01/69	CRTSY	WASHINGTON U, MISSOURI	NC MEM HOSP, U OF FL
BLALOCK	TULLY T.	11/01/68	HONRY	EMORY UNIVERSITY	MASS MEM HOSP.
BLEICH	ALLAN	04/01/69	ACTIV	EMORY UNIVERSITY	GEORGETOWN
BLOCK	DONALD	04/01/69	ACTIV	LSU	TOURO, LA
BOBO	EARL	01/01/72	CRTSY	EMORY UNIVERSITY	EMORY & GRADY
BOOTH	ARTHUR S.	09/01/72	ACTIV	MEDICAL COLLEGE OF GA	CITY OF MEMPHIS HOSP
BOURDEAUX	WARD C.	04/01/69	ACTIV	TULANE	CHARLETTE MEM. HOSP
BOWEN	EDWARD G.	12/01/69	ACTIV	DUKE	UNIV. OF FL, GRADY
BOYD	FRED D.	10/01/71	ASSOC	INFORMATION NOT ON FILE	
BREGMAN	LARRY	03/01/72	DECEA	EMORY UNIVERSITY	CHILDREN'S HOSP, MI
BROOKS	JAMES FRANK	06/01/71	CRTSY	MEDICAL COLLEGE OF GA	TALMADGE, EMORY
BROOME	HARRY L.	09/01/72	ACTIV	U OF N.C.	SCOTTISH RITE, GA
BROWN	HOWARD S.	04/01/69	ACTIV	INDIANA UNIV.	MARQUETTE
BROWN	NYDA W.	12/01/69	CRTSY	EMORY UNIVERSITY	TALMADGE HOSP.
BROWN	JIMMY S.	10/01/73	ACTIV	EMORY UNIVERSITY	GRADY
BRUNT, JR,	GWYNNE T.	10/01/73	ACTIV	EMORY UNIVERSITY	EMORY
BUNNEN	ROBERT L.	11/01/68	HONRY	EMORY UNIVERSITY	BOSTON CITY
BURNS	WILLIAM B.	06/01/71	RESIG	JOHN HOPKINS	YALE-NEW HAVEN HOSP
BUTLER	CHARLES	10/01/73	ACTIV	UNIV. OF MICHIGAN	ST. JOSEPH MERCY

CAHN	BERNARD J.	09/01/72	CRTSY	UNIV OF IOWA	DUKE, WAYNE STATE
CARLISLE	O.B.	05/01/69	CRTSY	VANDERBILT	TULANE
CARLOCK	KELLER S.	03/01/70	ACTIV	VANDERBILT	COLUMBIA, NY
CARRINGTON	LOUIE H.	03/01/70	DECEA	MC OF VA	GRADY
CARTER	JAMES A	10/10/70	CRTSY	DUKE	MC OF VA
CARTER	SANDY B., SR	03/01/70	HONRY	EMORY UNIVERSITY	CHARITY, NEW ORLEANS
CATANZARO	MARSHALL J.	06/01/70	ACTIV	ST. LOUIS UNIV.	ST JOHNS, KANSAS CITY
CHANDLER	NEAL	01/01/71	LAPSE	EMORY UNIVERSITY	EMORY
CLARK	NEWTON	01/01/72	ACTIV	U OF SC	GA BAPTIST
COHEN	DAVID M.	10/01/70	ACTIV	MEDICAL COLLEGE OF GA	MCG, UNIV HOSP, OHIO
COHEN	LAWRENCE	01/01/71	CRTSY	CHICAGO MED SCHOOL	MAIMONIDES MED CTR
COLLINS	WILLIAM C.	03/01/70	ACTIV	MEDICAL COLLEGE OF GA	GA BAPTIST, SCOTTISH
COOPER	HARRY A.	12/01/69	ACTIV	MEDICAL COLLEGE OF GA	PIEDMONT
COOPER	LAWRENCE	11/01/73	ACTIV	EMORY UNIVERSITY	GRADY
COTTS	LEONARD L.	11/01/68	ACTIV	MEDICAL COLLEGE OF GA	UNIV OF WASHINGTON
COWART	G. THOMAS	04/01/69	RESIG	EMORY UNIVERSITY	EMORY
CRIDER	HARRY	11/01/68	CRTSY	MEDICAL COLLEGE OF GA	CRAWFORD LONG
CROSS	JAMES L.	04/01/69	ACTIV	MEDICAL COLLEGE OF GA	GRADY
CURTIS	EARNEST M.	12/01/69	ACTIV	CORNELL	JOHNS HOPKIN
DALRYMPLE	DAVID E.	06/01/71	ACTIV	UNIV OF CHICAGO	UNIV OF IOWA
DAVIS	M. BEDFORD	09/01/72	HONOR	EMORY UNIVERSITY	EMORY, VA HOSP.
DAVIS	MARVIN L.	09/01/73	ACTIV	INFORMATION NOT ON FILE	
DAVIS	WARREN W.	12/01/69	ACTIV	VANDERBILT	NATIONAL HEART INST.
DEITCH	MILTON J.	11/01/68	ACTIV	WASHINGTON U.., MO	JEWISH HOSP, GRADY
DELAPERRIERE	ARMAND A.	09/01/71	ACTIV	MEDICAL COLLEGE OF GA	US ARMY TRIPLER HOSP
DENNISON	DAVID	04/01/69	RESIG	EMORY UNIVERSITY	GRADY
DOWDA	FREDRICK W.	11/01/68	CRTSY	EMORY UNIVERSITY	BARNES HOSP
DULOCK	MALCOLM	03/01/72	ASSOC	U OF TEXAS	
ECHEMENDIA	MARIANO M.	03/01/70	HONOR	U OF HAVANNA	ST JOSEPHS, IOWA
EDMONDSON	STEPHEN W.	03/01/71	RESIG	MEDICAL COLLEGE OF GA	U OF MD., EMORY
EHRLICH	JONATHAN S.	10/01/73	ACTIV	STATE U OF NY	U OF WISCONSIN
ENGEL	JOEL S.	09/01/72	ACTIV	U OF TEXAS	GRADY
ENGELHARDT	SAMUEL M	12/01/69	ACTIV	MC OF ALABAMA	JOHNS HOPKIN
EPSTEIN	JACOB	11/01/68	ACTIV	U OF TENNESEE	BARNES HOSP, ST LOUIS
ESPINOZA	FRANCISCO T	03/01/70	CRTSY	SAN FERNANDO MED SCHOOL	ST JOSEPHS
ESTES	JAMES W.	01/01/73	ACTIV	MEDICAL COLLEGE OF GA	U OF TENN
EUBANKS	OMER L.	11/01/68	CRTSY	EMORY UNIVERSITY	CRAWFORD LONG
EYZAGUIRRE	WILLIAM A	12/01/73	ACTIV	U OF ST MARK, PERU	PIEDMONT
FISHER	J. EDWARD	03/01/71	CRTSY	VANDERBILT	GA BAPTIST, GRADY
FISHER	WILLIAM R.	11/01/68	CRTSY	EMORY UNIVERSITY	LUTHERAN HOSP, OHIO
FORSYTH	DOUGLAS H.	04/01/69	ACTIV	TULANE	U.S.NAVAL-PA, GRADY
FOSTER	HARRY R.	07/01/73	CRTSY	MEDICAL COLLEGE OF GA	GRADY
FRANCO	NED M.	01/01/72	ACTIV	MEDICAL COLLEGE OF GA	EMORY, GRADY
FRANCO	RICHARD D.	09/01/71	ASSOC	EMORY UNIVERSITY	EMORY
FREEDMAN	MILTON H.	12/01/69	HONOR	EMORY UNIVERSITY	GRADY, PRATT DIAG
FREEMAN	LAWRENCE L.	11/01/68	RESIG	EMORY UNIVERSITY	CRAWFORD LONG
FUERST	JULIAN F.	11/01/68	CRTSY	U OF MICHIGAN	SINAI, GA BAPTIST
FULGHUM	CHARLES B.	11/01/68	CRTSY	U OF N.C.	N.C. MEM. HOSP.
FUNK	F. JAMES JR.	11/01/68	RESIG	EMORY UNIVERSITY	KENNEDY VA, BOSTON
GABLE	THOMAS W.	03/01/71	ACTIV	U OF NC.	US NAVY- PA, U OF PA
GALINA	MORTON P.	11/01/68	CRTSY	TUFTS	BRONX
GALLOWAY	WILLIAM H.	09/01/71	HONRY	U HOSP, AUGUSTA	GA BAPTIST
GARNER	ROBERT C.	09/01/71	ACTIV	WASHINGTON U.	ST LOUIS CHILDRENS
GAY	JAMES W.	11/01/68	ACTIV	MEDICAL COLLEGE OF GA	CRAWFORD LONG
GERLING	JOHN J.	11/01/68	ACTIV	U OF BUFFALO	E.J. MEYER
GILNER	DONALD M.	01/01/71	CRTSY	MEDICAL COLLEGE OF GA	ST CHRISTOPHERS, PA
GOLDSTEIN	MARTIN I.	04/01/69	CRTSY	U OF MIAMI	JACKSON MEM, VA-GA
GONZALEZ	LUIS	09/01/72	HONRY	UNIV OF LOUISVILLE	EMORY
GONZALEZ	VICTOR R.	06/01/70	CRTSY	TULANE	TULANE
GORDON	STEPHEN F.	10/01/70	ACTIV	U OF MD.	PA HOSP
GRAVES	RAPHAEL K.	03/01/70	ACTIV	EMORY UNIVERSITY	EMORY
GRAY	SAMUEL H.	06/01/71	ASSOC	MISSOUI UNIV.	MT. ZION, CALIFORNIA
GREENBERG	JOEL I	11/01/68	ACTIV	VANDERBILT	CRAWFORD LONG
GRISAMORE	JENNINGS M	03/01/70	HONRY	WASHINGTON UNIV.	GRADY, EMORY, VA
GRUMET	ROSS F.	12/01/69	RESIG	DOWNSTATE MED, NY	TOPEKA VA, MT SINAI
HALL	JOHN C.	12/01/69	ACTIV	EMORY UNIVERSITY	GRADY
HALLUM	ALTON V.	12/01/69	RESIG	EMORY UNIVERSITY	GRADY
HANCOCK	CHARLES I.	06/01/71	CRTSY	MEDICAL COLLEGE OF GA	SCOTTISH RITE
HARDCASTLE	WILLIAM R.	01/01/72	CRTSY	TULANE	OCHSNER CLINIC, LA
HARRISON	JOHN R.	12/01/69	CRTSY	MEDICAL COLLEGE OF GA	
HARTLEY	JOHN H	04/01/69	CRTSY	EMORY UNIVERSITY	EMORY
HARTRAMPF	CARL R.	11/01/68	CRTSY	NC MEM HOSP	WASHINGTON UNIV.
HAVERTY	JOHN R.	09/01/73	HONRY	INFORMATION NOT ON FILE	W
HAWK	JUDSON L.	11/01/68	LAPSE	MCG	ST CHRISTOPHER, PA
HECHT	HOWARD L.	03/01/71	ACTIV	U OF ILLINOIS	HINES V.A.
HEIN	DAVID E.	11/01/68	ACTIV	EMORY UNIVERSITY	GRADY, CINCINNATI
HENDRIX	VERNON J.	11/01/67	ACTIV	EMORY UNIVERSITY	GA BAPTIST
HILL	EUGENE A	09/01/72	ASSOC	EMORY UNIVERSITY	GA BAPTIST, U OF VA

HOOD	E. WALTER	11/01/68	CRSTY	MEDICAL COLLEGE OF GA	PIEDMONT
HORNSTEIN	STEPHEN L.	09/01/71	CRTSY	UNIV. OF LOUISVILLE	EMORY
HUTCHINSON	JOSEPH R.	01/01/72	CRTSY	U OF VA	MED U OF S.C.
JAFFE	STEVEN L.	09/01/73	CRTSY	A EINSTEIN COL OF MED.	MASS MENTAL HEALTH
JAMES	W. SCOTT	11/01/68	ACTIV	DUKE	BOSTON CHILDRENS
JANTER	THOMAS B	03/01/72	ACTIV	U OF MICHIGAN	GRADY
JOHNSON	J. TRIMBLE	11/01/68	CRTSY	EMORY UNIVERSITY	BELLEVUE, GRADY
JOHNSON	R. JULIAN	09/01/71	CRTSY	EMORY UNIVERSITY	CRAWFORD LONG
JOHNSON	RAY L.	09/01/71	CRTSY	MEDICAL COLLEGE OF GA	MCG
JONES	ARTHUR B.	10/01/70	CRTSY	U OF ARKANSAS	VANDERBILT,ST JOSEPH
JONES	RICHARD B.	11/01/68	ACTIV	EMORY UNIVERSITY	DC GEN, PIEDMONT
KAHN	ERIC M	03/01/71	CRTSY	JEFFERSON MED. COLLEGE	VA HOSP
KAUFMANN	JAMES A.	11/01/68	CRTSY	U OF TENN.	NEW ENGLAND MEDICAL
KEENER	ELLIS B.	04/01/69	RESIG	EMORY UNIVERSITY	MONTREAL NEURO INS
KILEY	JAMES D	10/01/73	CRTSY	EMORY UNIVERSITY	GRADY
KINDY	KEN D.	01/01/73	CRTSY	INDIANA UNIV.	INDIANA UNIV.
KING	C. RICHARD	07/01/73	RESIG	U OF TENN	W OK. TB SANITARIUM
KLOTZ	HUGH A.	11/01/68	CRTSY	MEDICAL COLLEGE OF GA	GA BAPTIST
KRAL	ROBERT	09/01/71	HONOR	GEORGETOWN MED.	GRADY
KRAMER	JOHN H.	07/01/73	ACTIV	ST. LOUIS UNIV.	UNITED HOSPS, NJ
KRUGMAN	PHILIP I.	11/01/68	RESIG	EMORY UNIVERSITY	GRADY, EMORY
LAHMAN	ROSE A.	03/01/71	RESIG	U OF TORONTO	HOSP FOR CHRONIC, NY
LAMIS	PANO A.	06/01/70	RESIG	MC OF SC	MC OF SC
LANDY	MICHAEL S.	06/01/71	CRTSY	A EINSTEIN	JACKSON MEM
LANGFORD	JAMES F.	11/01/68	CRTSY	EMORY UNIVERSITY	WILMINGTON HOSP, DE
LANIER	BOB G.	06/01/70	ACTIV	MEDICAL COLLEGE OF GA	MAYO
LEE	JOHN E.	10/01/73	ACTIV	DUKE	U OF WASHINGTON, NY
LEVENSON	DAVID S.	04/01/69	CRTSY	U OF MICHIGAN	DUKE
LEVINE	MICHAEL K.	01/01/68	ACTIV	TUFTS	BOSTON
LEVINE	RAPHAEL S.	09/01/72	LAPSE	STATE U OF NY	MAIMONIDES, VA-CALIF
LEVINE	STANLEY	07/01/69	ACTIV	MEDICAL COLLEGE OF GA	MADIGAN GEN HOSP, WA
LEVITAS	THEODORE C	03/01/72	RESIG	EMORY UNIVERSITY	EMORY
LINDSEY, JR.,	I. LEE	03/01/70	ACTIV	MEDICAL COLLEGE OF GA	GRADY
MACRIS	ALLEN	03/01/70	ACTIV	EMORY UNIVERSITY	PIEDMONT, ATLANTA VA
MAGEE	KENNETH	09/10/71	ACTIV	UNIV. OF MD	JOHN HOPKINS
MARCHMAN	MARVIN	03/01/70	RESIG	UNIV. OF TENN.	METHODIST HOSP, TENN
MARGESON	RICHARD	11/01/68	HONOR	EMORY UNIVERSITY	EMORY
MATHEWS	W. STANLEY	09/10/71	RESIG	EMORY UNIVERSITY	GA BAPTIST
MATTISON	RICHARD C	09/10/72	ACTIV	EMORY UNIVERSITY	EMORY
MAYER	W. BREM	06/01/70	CRTSY	DUKE	GRADY
MCCOY	JOHN	11/01/68	ACTIV	DUKE	WASHINGTON,D.C.,
MCCUISTON	C. FRED	11/01/68	ACTIV	EMORY UNIVERSITY	D.C. GENERAL
MCDONOUGH	L. ALLEN	09/01/71	ACTIV	EMORY UNIVERSITY	EMORY
MCGINNIS	LAMAR	04/01/69	CRTSY	MEDICAL COLLEGE OF GA	U. OF TEXAS
MCGRAW	WALKER C.	03/01/72	CRTSY	MEDICAL COLLEGE OF GA	
MCKEE	DAVID S.	03/01/72	CRTSY	U. OF VA	GRADY
MCLEAN	DONALD C.	01/01/71	CRTSY	CORNELL	N.Y. HOSP.
MESSER	ALFRED	03/01/71	HONRY	COLUMBIA UNIV.	VA HOSP, NY STATE
MILLER	GEORGE	12/01/69	ACTIV	MEDICAL COLLEGE OF GA	DUKE
MILLER	PRESTON	11/01/68	ACTIV	EMORY UNIVERSITY	ATLANTA, VA
MINOR	JAMES B.	11/01/68	ACTIV	U. OF ARKANSAS	ST. LOUIS CITY
MITCHELL	JAMES	11/01/68	ACTIV	EMORY UNIVERSITY	DUKE
MITCHELL	WILLIAM E.	03/01/70	RESIG	JOHNS HOPKIN	JOHNS HOPKIN
MOLKNER	KENNETH C	12/01/71	CRTSY	YALE	CHARITY HOSP, LA
MOORE	B. WALDO	12/01/69	RESIG	EMORY UNIVERSITY	ATLANTA, VA
MOORE	WILLIAM W.	11/01/69	HONRY	INFORMATION NOT ON FILE	
MORAN	MARTIN	01/01/71	ACTIV	U. OF TENNESSEE	WM. BEAUMONT, TEXAS
MORTON	WILLIAM	06/01/70	CRTSY	U. OF MIAMI	GRADY
MOYER	LEROY	09/01/71	ACTIV	EMORY UNIVERSITY	GRADY
MURRAY	WALTER A.,JR	11/01/68	DECEA	CORNELL	COLUMBUS CHILDRENS
MUSSER	ELLYN ZUNKER	09/01/72	ACTIV	U. OF ILL	GRADY
MYERS	WALTER L.	04/01/69	RESIG	U. OF PA	OCHSNER HOSP, LA
NEELD	JOHN B., JR	10/01/73	ACTIV	VANDERBILT	EMORY
NEWTON, III	ZACHARIAH B.	01/01/71	ACTIV	JEFFERSON MED, PA	DUKE
NINCIC	ALEXANDER	01/01/72	LAPSE	WHITE PLAINS, NY	ST JOSEPH'S, ATLANTA
PALAY	BERNARD H.	11/01/68	CRTSY	EMORY UNIVERSITY	ATLANTA VA, EMORY
PAYNE	PETER	09/01/71	HONRY	MEDICAL COLLEGE OF GA	MCG
PEACOCK	LAMAR	04/01/69	RESIG	MEDICAL COLLEGE OF GA	UNIV. HOSP., AUGUSTA
PEARCE	T. ELDER	11/01/68	ACTIV	EMORY UNIVERSITY	PIEDMONT, GA BAPTIST
PENDERGRAST	WILLIAM J.	03/01/70	RESIG	EMORY UNIVERSITY	GRADY, CRAWFORD LONG
PENNINGTON	E. EARL	07/01/73	ACTIV	TULANE	CHARITY HOSP, LA
PEREZ	ANTONIO R.	06/01/70	CRTSY	HAVANA, CUBA	GRADY
PERKINSON	NEIL G.	04/01/69	CRTSY	BOWMAN GRAY	NEW YORK
PERLING	DAVID S.	11/01/68	ACTIV	MEDICAL COLLEGE OF GA	ST. SINAI, GRADY
PHILLIPS	WENDELL	09/01/72	ASSOC	MC OF SC	MC OF CENTRAL GA
PINTO	ALBERT P.	10/01/70	ACTIV	EMORY UNIVERSITY	GRADY
PITTMAN	FRANK S.	01/01/73	CRTSY	EMORY UNIVERSITY	EMORY
POOLE	ROBERT N.	06/01/72	ACTIV	INDIANA UNIV.	GEORGIA BAPTIST
POUND	EDWIN C.,JR	11/01/68	ASSOC	EMORY UNIVERSITY	PIEDMONT, DUKE
PRATER	R. BURT, JR	06/01/70	CRTSY	UNIV. OF ALABAMA	

PRESTON	E. NOEL	10/01/70	ACTIV	EMORY UNIVERSITY	GA BAPTIST, FLORIDA
PRUETT	JAMES E.	11/01/68	ACTIV	MEDICAL COLLEGE OF GA	GA BAPTIST, ENT HOSP
QUARTERMAN	KEITH A.	11/01/68	ACTIV	EMORY UNIVERSITY	MED. COL. HOSP, S.C.
QUILALA	EMILIANO P.	09/01/72	CRTSY	PHILIPPINES	NORTON MEM,KY PIEDMO
RAMSEY	JOHN E.	11/01/68	LAPSE	EMORY UNIVERSITY	PIEDMONT, U OF AR,OK
RAYEL	PETER A.	12/01/69	ACTIV	HARVARD	U. HOSP OF CLEVELAND
REISH	MARTIN L.	03/01/72	ACTIV	MEDICAL COLLEGE OF GA	GRADY
REITT	J. PETER	10/01/73	RESIG	DUKE	EMORY
RICCARDI	LOUIS	11/01/68	HONRY	MIDDLESEX UNIV.	ST. JOSEPH, VA-GA
RICHMAN	GARY O.	01/01/72	ACTIV	MEDICAL COLLEGE OF GA	HENRY FORD
RICHMOND	LEA	01/01/68	ACTIV	EMORY UNIVERSITY	GRADY, VA HOSP-GA
RICKS	HENRY C.	04/01/69	RESIG	JEFFERSON MED., PA	CINCINNATI GEN. HOSP
RIVKIN	LAURENCE M.	03/01/70	ACTIV	U. OF LOUISVILLE, KY	LOUISVILLE GEN. HOSP
ROSENBERG	RAYMOND	10/01/73	ACTIV	GEORGETOWN	GRADY
ROTHENBERG	MARVIN B.	11/01/68	ASSOC	TULANE	CHARITY HOSP, LA
RUBENSTEIN	ARNOLD	12/01/69	ASSOC	CHICAGO	MAYO, HINES VA- ILL.
RUSSELL	R. JAMES	04/01/69	ASSOC	MC OF ALABAMA	PHILA. GEN HOSP
SANDERS	C. VERNON	11/01/68	ACTIV	DUKE	GEORGETOWN
SANDERS	STEVEN L.	10/01/70	ACTIV	EMORY UNIVERSITY	EMORY/GRADY/VA
SCHATTEN	WILLIAM E.	11/01/68	RESIG	EMORY UNIVERSITY	UNIV. HOSP,CLEVELAND
SCHELLACK	JOHN K.	03/01/71	CRTSY	TULANE	CRAWFORD LONG
SCHWARTZ	SANFORD H.	06/01/72	ACTIV	STATE UNIV. OF N.Y.	STATE UNIV. OF N.Y.
SELMONOSKY	CARLOS	01/01/72	RESIG	U. OF BUENOS AIRES	BRONX,LONDON,IOWA
SHANKS	JAMES Z.	06/01/70	ACTIV	MEDICAL COLLEGE OF GA	GRADY
SHESSEL	HERBERT L.	11/01/68	CRTSY	SW MEDICAL, TX	ST. JOSEPHS,CRAWFORD
SHIVERS	OLIN	09/01/71	ACTIV	CORNELL	DUKE
SHMERLING	SANFORD A.	06/01/70	CRTSY	MEDICAL COLLEGE OF GA	MT SINAI,CRILE VA,OH
SHULER	ROBERT K.	11/01/68	CRTSY	EMORY UNIVERSITY	CINCINNATI CHILDRENS
SILVER	WILLIAM E.	03/01/71	ACTIV	MEDICAL COLLEGE OF GA	MT. SINAI-NY, NYU
SILVERSTEIN	CHARLES M	11/01/68	ACTIV	EMORY UNIVERSITY	GRADY/EMORY
SKARDASIS	GEORGE M	03/01/72	RESIG	U OF ATHENS, GREECE	CRAWFORD LONG
SLUTSKY	MORTON	01/01/72	ACTIV	TULANE	UNIV. OF PA
SMILACK	ZALE H	03/01/72	ACTIV	EMORY UNIVERSITY	OHIO
SMILEY	DAVID T.	11/01/68	HONOR	MEDICAL COLLEGE OF GA	GRADY
SMILEY	RUSSELL B	03/01/72	RESIG	MC OF VA	ROANOKE MEM HOSP
SMITH	RICHARD B.	11/01/68	ACTIV	DUKE	BABIES HOSP, NY
SOMMERVILLE	MARGARET J.	03/01/70	CRTSY	U. OF IOWA	
SORIANO	MARIA J.	09/01/71	RESIG	UNIV. OF MEXICO	ST. JOSEPH'S, GA
SPANIER	JACOB A.	11/01/68	ACTIV	MC - SC	GRADY
ST. LOUIS	JOSEPH A, JR	11/01/68	ACTIV	GEORGETOWN	WALTER REED
STAATS	ETHAN F.	04/01/69	CRTSY	EMORY UNIVERSITY	GRADY
STEVES	ELMA M.	11/01/68	ACTIV	SAN MARCOS, PERU	ST JOSEPHS, PIEDMONT
STRICKLAND	GRADY	09/01/71	CRTSY	MEDICAL COLLEGE OF GA	MACON HOSP.
SYRIBEYS	JOHN P	04/01/69	RESIG	EMORY UNIVERSITY	PIEDMONT, ST JOSEPHS
SZECSEY	ALEXANDER	11/01/68	HONRY	INFORMATION NOT ON FILE	
TAYLOR	DAVID M.	12/02/69	ACTIV	U. OF ILL.	USA, TEXAS
TAYLOR	JOHN E., JR	01/01/72	RESIG	EMORY UNIVERSITY	CRAWFORD, EGLESTON
TENENBAUM	STANLEY M.	06/01/72	CRTSY	EMORY UNIVERSITY	UNIV. OF CA
THEBAUT	BEN R.	11/01/68	HONRY	EMORY UNIVERSITY	DADE COUNTY FL,GRADY
THIO	RICHARD	01/01/73	ACTIV	UNIV. UTRECHT NETHERLANDS	
THOMAS	KENNETH	06/01/72	CRTSY	DARTMOUTH, STANFORD	U. OF MINN., VA CNTR
THOMPSON	CHARLES W.	04/01/69	CRTSY	EMORY UNIVERSITY	VA-GA
THRONE	MARTIN L.	03/01/73	ACTIV	U. OF ONTARIO, CANADA	MCGILL UNIV, CANADA
TOOLE	WILLIAM N	11/01/68	ACTIV	EMORY UNIVERSITY	JOHNS HOPKIN
TORRANCE	CLARENCE B.	03/01/70	ACTIV	EMORY UNIVERSITY	GRADY
TROPAUER	ALAN	03/01/71	CRTSY	NYU	U. OF CINCINNATI
VAN DE WETERING	ROBERT J.	11/01/68	RESIG	U OF TENN	INDIANA U, US NAVAL
VANDERPOOL	GERALD E.	06/01/71	RESIG	U OF LOUISVILLE, KY	U OF TENN.
VANDIVER	ROY W.	04/01/69	RESIG	MEDICAL COLLEGE OF GA	GRADY, NC MEM. HOSP.
VELKOFF	ABRAHAM S.	01/01/71	RESIG	EMORY UNIVERSITY	EMORY
VITNER	SAUL	11/01/68	ACTIV	EMORY UNIVERSITY	ST. LOUIS MATERNITY
WAITS	EDWARD J.	11/01/68	ACTIV	EMORY UNIVERSITY	PIEDMONT
WALKER	EXUM B.	12/01/69	HONRY	EMORY UNIVERSITY	NY AREA HOSPITALS(4)
WALL	WILLIAM H.	04/01/69	CRTSY	EMORY UNIVERSITY	JACKSON MEM. HOSP.
WEST	JAY HERBERT	11/01/68	ACTIV	BOWMAN GRAY	CHICAGO PRES, MCG
WHALEY	WILLIAM H.	09/01/72	CRTSY	MEDICAL COLLEGE OF GA	GRADY
WHITE	WILLIAM P.	07/01/73	CRTSY	EMORY UNIVERSITY	GRADY, CHILDRENS
WHITNEY	DOUGLASS G.	11/01/68	CRTSY	TULANE	HENRY FORD
WHYTE	DANA F.	10/01/70	ACTIV	U OF MICHIGAN	U OF MICHIGAN
WIEGAND	STEWART E.	06/01/71	ACTIV	BAYLOR	
WILDSTEIN	GILBERT	11/01/68	RESIG	STATE UNIV OF NY	MT. SINAI, ALBANY
WILDSTEIN	WALTER	11/01/68	CRTSY	NORTHWESTERN	MT. SINAI
WILLIAMS	J. DAVID	03/01/70	ACTIV	EMORY UNIVERSITY	GRADY
WILLS	S. ANGIER	11/01/68	CRTSY	EMORY UNIVERSITY	EMORY
WILSON	HENRY H	03/01/72	RESIG	U OF NAGPUR, INDIA	ST. JOSEPH'S, GA
WILSON	JOHN P.	03/01/70	CRTSY	MEDICAL COLLEGE OF GA	UNIV. HOSP.
WINNER	JONATHAN D.	12/01/71	ACTIV	U OF IOWA	CINCINNATI GEN HOSP.
WINTER	THORNE	11/01/68	ACTIV	HARVARD	PETER BENT BRIGHAM
WOOD	R WARNER, JR	11/01/68	CRTSY	U OF VA	ST. LUKE'S
WOODSON	GRATTAN C,JR	11/01/68	CRTSY	EMORY UNIVERSITY	NYU
ZAKARIA	MAJED	03/01/73	ACTIV	DAMASCUS UNIV, SYRIA	EMORY
ZWEIG	ARNOLD	01/01/72	CRTSY	CHICAGO	NORTHWESTERN
ZWIREN	GERALD T.	11/01/68	CRTSY	MC OF VA	NORFOLK GEN HOSP

APPENDIX THREE
Members of Board of Trustees

Hospital Authority of Fulton County or Northside Hospital, Inc. 1966 to Present

Acquaviva, Ellen 6/85-11/90, Chair. 1990
Adams, Eugene E. 1970-1980 (Treasurer, non-voting member)
Askew, Wilburn 9/72-1982, Chair. 1974-1977
Bardi, G.B. 9/74-9/82
Barfield, Julian J.* 1966-1969, 1969-1973
Blalock, Dr. Tully* 1966-1968, 1968-1972
Booth, Dr. Arthur 9/82-8/87
Breman, William 1966-1976
Brooks, Wilson 12/71-6/72
Buckley, Ferdinand 1982-1990, Chair. 1987-1989
Bunnen, Dr. Robert L. 1974-1981
Canning, William C. 1977-1985, Chair. 1983-1985
Carter, William F.* 1966-1974, Chair. 2/72-6/73
Cates, Charles 10/72-1973
Chinlund, Daniel K.* 1966-1/69
Cobb, Hollis L.* 1966-1970, Chair. 1966-2/70
Collins, Dr. William C. 1991-present
Common, Langdon 1971-1981
Croft, Edward S. III 1982-1990, Chair. 1988-1990
Densler, Dr. James F. 1980-1988
Deyo, William T., Jr. 1989-present, Chair. 1993-present
Egan, Maurice M. 2/69-3/70
Elson, Suzanne 7/87-1988
Gade, Marvin 1985-6/87
Garrett, Lu 11/82-7/87
Hamilton, Ellis D. 10/66-9/71
Harris, Elmer 1986-1989
Hathcock, Dr. Earl W. Jr. 10/72-7/74
Hills, Thomas D. 1981-1989, Chair. 1985-1987
Howlett, Richard J.* 1966
Kirschner, Sidney 1985-11/92 (Administrator and CEO 11/92 to present)
Lanier, Dr. Willis 1984-1987
Lee, Dr. John 1987-present
Lindsey, Archie L. 1/69-6/71, Chair. 2/70-6/71
Marquis, Jack D. 1971-1973, Chair. 1978-1980

McCoy, Dr. John 6/68-1972 (Secretary, non-voting member)
Miller, Dr. Preston 1985-1993
Mitchell, E.R., Jr. 1988-present
Neeld, Dr. John B., Jr. 1991-present
Pennington, Dr. E. Earl 1990-present
Rains, Thomas. N. 1978-1986, Chair. 1980-1983
Raney, Augustus M. 12/71-1977
Rayel, Dr. Peter 1980-1984
Richmond, Dr. Lea* 1966-1974; 1981-1985, Chair. 7/73-1974
Sanders, Dr. C. Vernon 1974-1982
Sehgal, R.K. 10/91-present
Shelton, Charles B., III 1990-present
Smulian, Betty R. 1989-present
Spanier, Dr. Jacob A. 1989-present, Chair. 1990-1993
Stone, Dr. Lawrence B. 1993-present
Swensson, Luther E. 1966-6/68
Teuscher, John 1970-2/72, Chair. 7/71-2/72
Travis, William 12/76-11/82
Turman, John 12/74-1978
Van de Wetering, Dr. Robert J. 12/74-1980
Westbrook, William L. 1989-present
Woodson, Dr. Grattan C., Jr. 1972-1974 (Secretary, non-voting member)

*Designates original Hospital Authority Board
Northside Hospital Inc. was created in 1991 restructuring

APPENDIX FOUR

Appendix 4	LIST OF PAST CHIEFS OF STAFF SINCE NORTHSIDE HOSPITAL OPENED	
PHYSICIAN NAME	DATES OF SERVICE	SPECIALTY
Keith Quarterman, M.D.	1969 – 1970	General Surgery
C. Vernon Sanders, M.D.	1970 – 1971	Internal Medicine
Earl W. Hathcock, M.D.	1971 – 1972	OB\GYN
Robert Van De Wetering, M.D.	1972 – 1973	Psychiatry
David Cohen, M.D.	1973 – 1974	ENT Surgery
John Hall, M.D.	1974 – 1975	Intenal Medicine
W. Scott James, M.D.	1975 – 1976	Pediatrics
Carl Hartrampf, M.D.	1976 – 1977	Plastic Surgery
William Avery, M.D.	1977 – 1978	OB\GYN
Newton Clark, M.D.	1978 – 1979	Orthopedic Surgery
Gordon Azar, M.D.	1979 – 1980	Internal Medicine
Thomas Gable, M.D.	1980 – 1981	Psychiatry
Milton Goldman, M.D.	1981 – 1982	Urology
John Patton, M.D.	1\82 – 10\82	Anesthesia
Dennis Lee, M.D.	1982 – 1983	Orthopedic Surgery
James Estes, M.D.	1983 – 1984	Vascular Surgery
John E. Lee, M.D.	1984 – 1986	Internal Medicine
Charles Rogers, M.D.	1986 – 5\87	OB\GYN
James Alexander, M.D.	5\87 – 1988	Pediatrics
E. Earl Pennington, M.D.	1988 – 1990	General Surgery
Lawrence B. Stone, M.D.	1990 – 1992	Perinatology\Radiology
Edward G. Bowen, M.D.	1992 – 1994	OB\GYN
Gwynne Brunt, M.D.	1994 – 1996	Radiology

APPENDIX FIVE

Appendix 5 — NORTHSIDE HOSPITAL EMPLOYEES WITH 20+ YEARS OF SERVICE

PROFESSIONAL NURSES

Name	HIRE DATE
Absuaid, Harriet	12\21\70
Bond, Jean	03\26\73
Bowman, Nancy	09\04\73
Brown, Nancy	07\13\70
Callais, Gail	09\10\73
Cronk, Suzanne	06\25\73
Dawkins, William	01\17\72
Dawson, William	07\09\73
Ehlers, Nancy	09\27\71
Estes, Aldeena	10\01\73
Flake, Jane	11\12\70
Gabert, Marlene	07\13\70
Gelly, Dolores	07\13\70
Giegerich, Carole	09\14\70
Graff, Jacqueline	07\06\70
Hardiman, Flora	10\01\73
Harry, Anne	09\28\70
Hindle, Nancy	01\23\73
Ivey, Juanita	06\29\70
Kinnard, Shirley	06\29\70
Kremmer, Dona	06\07\70
Maloney, Denise	07\02\73
Reese, Dorothy	07\27\70
Roberts, Cynthia	08\28\72
Rockswold, Mirtle	09\03\73
Ruttle, Elizabeth	11\22\71
Smith, Holly	05\10\71
Sohn, Myung	08\26\72
Stevenson, Margaret	08\30\71
Stowell, Patricia	10\05\70
Swindle, Teresa	03\13\72
Szczupak, Sophia	08\14\73
Talbott, Cumi	04\24\73
Turley, Caroline	09\18\72
Twiner, Evelyn	10\09\73
Waits, Nancy	09\13\71
Westbrook, Maryann	07\06\70

MANAGERS

Name	HIRE DATE
Autry, Billy	08\13\73
Chastain, June	06\01\70
Cheatham, Janis	02\14\72
Cook, Margaret	04\24\72
Kervin, Rufus	06\15\70
Martin, Mary	12\04\70
Stokes, Phyllis	07\13\70
Thomas, Linda	08\30\71
Walker, Ted	05\10\71

PHARMACIST

Name	HIRE DATE
Poe, Jane	03\26\73

ADMINISTRATIVE SERVICES

Name	HIRE DATE
Alexander, Emily	10\26\70
Barksdale, Frances	08\13\73
Blackman, Vicky	01\17\72
Brady, Rita	08\06\73
Bryant, Mae	06\29\70
Coggins, Kathryn	08\16\71
Derrett, Catherine	01\18\73
Farmer, Helen	06\30\70
Foley, Joyce	03\01\73
Francis, Charles	01\22\73
Garner, Barbara	08\23\71
Garner, Sue	09\19\73
Harlin, Linda	09\19\73
Harrell, Marusha	09\25\73
Hays, Barbara	09\07\71
Hill, Betty	05\29\73
Hiscock, Roberta	06\08\70
Hodo, Leila	07\13\70
Howard, Jayne	05\07\73
Jackson, Mary	09\19\70
Jenkins, Bernice	01\30\73
Johnson, Nellie	06\29\70
Knuckles, Ernestine	02\06\73
Lawrence Constance	01\07\71
Marshman, Valina	08\15\73
McMillian, Patricia	09\13\71
McWright, Sarah	10\11\71
Murray, Irene	09\10\73
Murray, Jean	10\22\73
Pfrangle, Mary	10\17\72
Phillips, Linda	01\02\73
Pritchett, Joanne	06\29\70
Pruitt, Sandra	05\30\73
Ragsdale, Beatrice	06\28\70
Roberts, Royce	09\28\70
Starling, Starling	03\17\72
Strickland, Nevie	09\28\73
Thomas, Henry	07\31\73
Tolbert, Anette	10\25\71
Wallace, Odessa	03\01\72
Whitcomb, Gladys	03\17\71
Wilson, Harold	08\24\70
Woods, OJ	09\29\70

PROFESSIONAL SERVICES

Name	HIRE DATE
Bacon, Marie	11\01\71
Cleveland, Barbara	08\03\70
Contes, Adra	12\01\71
Harris, Josie	07\13\70
Henderson, Marie	09\24\72
King, Ann	11\19\72
Levine, Susan	10\31\73
Martin, Millard	02\28\72
McCoy, Allene	08\03\70
Roberts, Mary	06\18\73
Roberts, Mattie	08\13\73
Turner, Sandra	09\24\73
Willingham, Lana	10\16\72
Wimberly, Aurie	09\27\71

APPENDIX SIX
More About The Auxiliary

At the 23rd anniversary celebration in 1993, total membership was 772 (442 active, 251 associate, 58 life members and 84 Volunteens), working in 36 areas of the hospital:

Auxiliary Office
    Receptionists
Assistants to
    the Chaplain
Baby Pictures
Blood Drive
Cancer Center
Community Health
    Education:
    – Puppet Shows (3)
    – Tours
Education
Emergency Room
Employee Health
Escort
Flower Delivery
Gift Cart
Gift Shop
Home Health
Hospice

ICU/CCU
Information
Labor and Delivery
Library Cart
Mail Room
Medical Library
Newborn Nursery
Occupational Therapy
Pain Clinic
Patient Relations
Personnel
Pharmacy
Physical Therapy
Post-Anesthesia
Radiology
Special Services
Speech Pathology
Surgery Prep
Volunteens
Women's Center

The following members have received their 20-year pins, representing a minimum of 100 hours of service for 20 consecutive years: Loretta Bruce, Nancy Carson, Ida Lee Cheves, Jean Durden, Candee Elrod, Grace Everett, Rosemary Fox, Ardyth Geigel, Betty Henneke, Louis Henneke, Mimi Hogan, Jeannine Johnston, Lois Kirk, Jean Mason, Doris McLeod, Maxine Overby, Sally Patterson, Marilyn Powell, Mary Roche, Doris Schilling, Rosemary Smither, Betty Thomas, Janet Torrence, Della Walser and Janet Wills.

In Northside's 23 years, members gave an estimated total of 1,112,001 hours of service, plus $2,505,000 in pledges and gifts.

The Gift Shop, the first profit-making service, opened in 1970. The inventory for the shop was purchased with a $1,250 loan from the hospital. The shop was moved several times, once into a trailer in the upper parking lot. It has been in its present location since 1986.

Baby Pictures, the second profit-making service, was established in January 1973. Newborns are photographed daily. In the beginning the pictures were hand delivered to the mothers before their discharge; now the photograph package is mailed to the family due to the short hospital stay of most mothers.

In 1972 the auxiliary began sponsoring the training of Volunteens (boys and girls, ages 13-18) to assist the auxiliary and hospital personnel in auxiliary services and patient care. Starting with the Christmas of 1972, all Christmas babies have been sent home in a large felt stocking, a gift from the auxiliary.

The Assistants to the Chaplain service was launched in January 1974 at the request of the hospital. The auxilians considered this very significant. The first of its kind, it has been copied throughout the Southeast.

The auxiliary's first educational outreach service to the community was developed in 1977 in the form of puppetry programs. These proved quite popular and now three different shows are presented throughout the school year to elementary and preschoolers in Cobb, Fulton, DeKalb and Gwinnett counties. In 1993 the auxiliary purchased a van to transport the puppeteers and their equipment into the community to present the shows (as well as to transport members to meetings in and out of town).

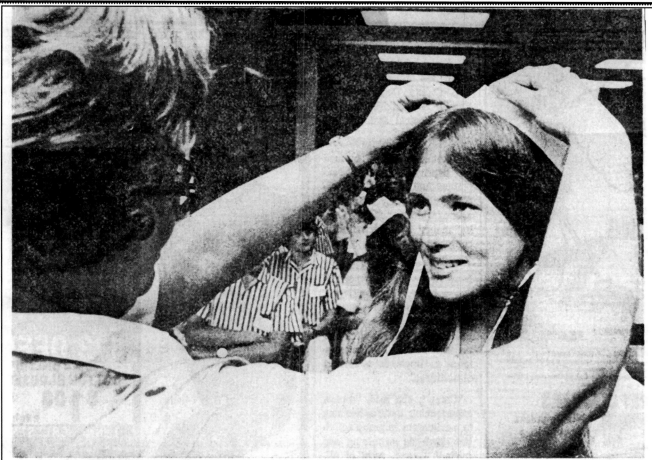

Staff Photo—George Clark

NORTHSIDE GETS NEW VOLUNTEENS

Kathy Hatchcock (right) is one of 29 Northside Hospital Volunteens who were capped at ceremonies in the Northside Hospital Mental Health Auditorium. The girls received caps and the boys got pins for completing their first 25 hours of service to the hospital. There are 100 boys and girls, ages 14-18, in the program with more than 65 on the waiting list. They are trained to help Pink Ladies and hospital personnel in auxiliary services, patient care and fiscal affairs. The program is sponsored by the Northside Auxillary of which Mrs. Jack Elrod, also shown here, is president.

NORTHSIDE HOSPITAL PINK LADIES ATTENDED COUNCIL ON AUXILIARIES WORKSHOP FOR VOLUNTEERS
Chaplain Dan Keels With (L-R) Mmes. Durden, Elrod, Murray, Bruce, Yarbrough, Everett and Fox

Neighbor Photo by Steve Hutcheson
JEANETTE DEMPSEY AND 'DR. NORTHSIDE' ENTERTAIN, AND EDUCATE, WITH UNIQUE CHILDREN'S SHOW
Northside Hospital Auxiliary Created Program To Show Children They Have Nothing To Fear From Doctors

APPENDIX SEVEN
Northside Hospital Foundation

The foundation has become an increasingly important and valuable appendage of the hospital under the leadership of Ken Kenton, whom Don Hutton appointed in March 1989.

It had been incorporated four years earlier under Chris Clark as a "501 (c) (3), publicly supported organization for the purposes of soliciting, collecting and receiving gifts, grants and contributions; managing assets and investments; and delivering and distributing money and property to and for the benefit of Northside Hospital."

The initial three directors comprising the foundation board were three former chairmen of the hospital board: Thomas H. Rains, William Canning and Dr. Lea Richmond. Tony Ziner, previously the executive director for development for St. Mary's Hospital in Saginaw, Michigan, was appointed executive vice-president in charge. At that time the foundation had a hard time hitting its stride. The hospital had completed a somewhat controversial fund-raising drive in 1985, and the foundation was not a priority in Clark's last years. Ziner was able to complete only part of a $3 million expansion and modernization capital campaign. The board did not meet a second time until June 1988, after Hutton had arrived, and Ziner resigned in October of that year.

Kenton previously served as director of development for the Emory University Business School and director of estate planning for Sweet Briar College. Previously, for 17 years he had been a nationally recognized manager and estate planning specialist with the Metropolitan Life Insurance Company.

Under Kenton, board vacancies were filled with influential community leaders. (Dr. David Cohen was the first new chairman in 1989.) Now the foundation has a governing board of 22 trustees and an advisory board of 60. In the past fiscal year donations increased to $560,000, with an additional $250,000 from the auxiliary in 1992-93 and $155,000 in donated services and supplies.

Hundreds of community leaders have become involved with Northside as they became fund-raising event volunteers, and Northside has become much more visible in local publications, radio and TV, as a result of exposure related to these events. Some of these have become well known among the public as well as financially successful: the Northside Ball ($240,000 net in 1992), Tree of Lights ($32,000 net in 1992) and the Golf Classic (a first-time event that netted $46,000 in 1992).

Kenton was promoted to president and CEO of the foundation in November 1990. Under the hospital reorganization in 1991, the foundation remains one of the three corporate entities under the umbrella of Northside Health Services, Inc. The current chairman of the board is attorney Robert E. Whitley, who has been a member since 1988.

APPENDIX EIGHT
More About Saint Joseph's

The Organization: The new Saint Joseph's Hospital, previously known as Saint Joseph's Infirmary, opened 6 1/2 years after Northside, in February 1978. In 1985, it adopted a corporate restructuring plan and became a member of the Eastern Mercy Health System (which incorporated in 1986). The EMHS is a Catholic health system founded by eight regional communities of the Sisters of Mercy, sponsoring 12 member healthcare organizations on the eastern seaboard from Maine to Florida. Seven of these, including the one in Atlanta and North Georgia, are holding companies with hospitals and other subsidiary corporations. In 1991, a "comprehensive strategic planning process" refined and revised St. Joseph's parent company, known as Mercy Health Services of the South, changing the name to St. Joseph's Health System. The SJHS is accountable to the Board of the Eastern Mercy Health System and to the Baltimore Community of the Sisters of Mercy.

In addition to St. Joseph's Hospital of Atlanta, the St. Joseph's Health System includes (1) St. Joseph's Hospital of Dahlonega, a 52-bed satellite hospital located about an hour away from Atlanta. Constructed in 1976, it was purchased from the Lumpkin County Hospital Authority in 1985 and is the only hospital in Lumpkin County.

(2) St. Joseph's Mercy Care Services, founded in December 1987 "to provide health care to the poor and underserved." Each of the three divisions represents one of the target populations: Hispanic Services provides bilingual medical care and medical referral services; Mercy Mobile Health Program delivers health care, education and social services to the homeless, and Senior Care offers adult day care, home care and employment services to the elderly in the Rome area.

(3) St. Joseph's Mercy Foundation was established in 1981. Similar to Northside's in function, it is the sole fund-raising entity for St. Joseph's Hospital of Atlanta and maintains endowments and support for not-for-profit activities.

Participation by St. Joseph's in the Eastern Mercy Health Systems has resulted in some shared services — in expenses such as mutual purchasing, creation of its own insurance system and the sharing of expertise in areas such as quality assurance programs.

Clinical Programs: When it moved to the northside campus, St. Joseph's was best known for its work in cardiology and cardiovascular services, and, to a lesser extent, for its interest in neurosurgery.

Heart and Cardiovascular Services: These began in 1965 with Dr. Arnoldo Fiedotin, who did the first coronary angiogram there in 1967. In 1970 he developed the pacemaker clinic, the third in the U.S. In 1979 he performed the first transluminal coronary angioplasty, as an alternative to bypass surgery, in the Southeast. (At that time this procedure was being performed at only five other medical facilities in the world.) Fiedotin and the Atlanta Cardiology Group, which he heads, have contributed significantly to the rapid development of cardiology in this area. St. Joseph's now has five cath labs. It acquired the first PET (positive emission tomography) scanner at a non-university hospital in the country. This non-invasive diagnostic tool can be used to detect coronary artery disease.

The Heart Institute is one of the busiest cardiac centers in the country. The first hospital in the Southeast to perform open heart surgery, St. Joseph's now annually performs more than any other hospital in Georgia. It is one of the relatively few hospitals in the nation approved to perform coronary atherectomy, a procedure that loosens and removes plaque from inside the walls of the coronary arteries. In 1992 doctors in the Heart Institute performed more than 1,900 open heart procedures and 3,200 angioplasties.

In 1991 St. Joseph's was one of four hospitals in the country designated by HCFA (Health Care Financing Administration) to participate in its successful, groundbreaking Coronary Bypass Demonstration Project to reduce health care costs while maintaining high quality of care.

Two years earlier it established the Heart Network, which now links 18 Georgia and North Carolina hospitals with cardiac specialists and advanced facilities at St. Joseph's. The goal of the network is to save patients by reducing the time between onset of heart attack symptoms and the delivery of appropriate intervention techniques.

The general public became more aware of the heart transplant program when cardiac surgeon Doug Murphy left Emory to come to St. Joseph's. The program is one of the busiest in the country. More than 200 heart transplants have been performed by the transplant team to date — an average of 25 each year — with an impressive one-year survival rate of 83.5 percent.

Cancer: Like Northside, over the years St. Joseph's has developed a fine Oncology service, which is now one of its three main areas of emphasis. It is one of 63 hospitals in the country designated by the National Cancer Institute as a Community Clinical Oncology Program (CCOP). It is the only facility in Georgia approved by the NCI to deliver the promising anticancer drug Taxol to women with ovarian cancer.

In 1992 St. Joseph's received CON approval to build a freestanding Cancer Center and its board recently approved a four to six-story building for consolidating and upgrading Oncology. There has been a significant development in 1993 resulting from the new climate on The Hill; the administrations and the boards at St. Joseph's and Northside are working actively and closely together to prevent overlap and needless expenditures and toward providing oncology on a shared services basis.

Orthopedics: This newest move in the hospital plan to diversify was given strong impetus when famed knee surgeon John Garrett and his Resurgens partners at Piedmont Hospital relocated their orthopedic practice to the top two floors (39,000 square feet) of the new center for specialty medicine at St. Joseph's. The hospital says it now has one of only five orthopedic specialists in the country who treat musculoskeletal sepsis and direct hyperbaric oxygen therapy, and that it is the only hospital in the Southeast where this type of treatment is available, with a success rate which is "unmatched." It also has one of the few orthopedic surgeons in the country experienced in handling "cold traumas," patients whose multiple fractures cannot be treated for more than 24 hours due to the life-threatening demands of their other injuries. The Garrett group of seven is in addition to the number of other orthopedists who practice at St. Joseph's.

APPENDIX NINE
More About Scottish Rite

History: Scottish Rite of Fremasonry is a fraternal organization which began in Europe over three centuries ago and first came to this country in Savannah, Georgia (some say Charleston, S.C.) over a century ago. It is based on the Masonic concept of "a belief in God, country and helping mankind." In 1914, Forrest Adair (of Adair Realty) and Mrs. William Wardlaw asked the organization to support efforts to build a hospital for crippled children, and it agreed to raise money to support the institution, which began in two small, wooden-frame rented cottages in Decatur in 1915, under the leadership of Dr. Michael Hoke.

Because of its pledge that it would always support the charity patient, the self-governing hospital was given the name Scottish Rite Hospital for Crippled Children. That is still its legal title. When it arrived on the campus opposite Northside, its scope broadened and it has since done business as the Scottish Rite Children's Medical Center (SRCMC).

Before 1965 it took care of only indigent patients. Dr. Wood Lovell, the third medical director, a very fine pediatric orthopedic surgeon, felt it was not right to discriminate against those with the ability to pay when they needed the very specialized skills and expertise that he and his experienced staff could provide, and the board allowed private patients and those covered by third party carriers. After Scottish Rite arrived at its new location in 1976, there began a marked increase in the proportion of private patients. Now, in 1993, only 8 1/2% of charges are from charity patients.

Dr. Raymond Morrissy is the fourth and present medical director. He took over this position when Lovell retired in 1983.

The Acute Care Center: Completed in 1991, it is one of the hospital's proud attractions, including ER (its first emergency section was built and staffed in 1984), an intensive care unit, new operative suites, and a large outpatient surgery. In 1987 it was designated by the State of Georgia as a Pediatric Trauma Unit, in an appropriate class.

Outreach: Scottish Rite now has an out-patient facility in Gwinnett County and provides after-hours pediatric emergency staffing for Cobb and Gwinnett hospitals.

Collaboration with Egleston Children's Hospital at Emory: For a number of years there has been intense competition between Atlanta's two children's hospitals, similar in many respects to the atmosphere on The Hill between St. Joseph's and Northside, but willing cooperative efforts are increasing. In June 1993 they entered a partnership venture to provide Home Health Care for children, pending approval of a CON.

For the past 10 years they have joined in a highly successful venture — the Children's Miracle Network Telethon (which raised about $1.25 million in 1992). Now a children's hospital in Macon and a developing children's hospital in Augusta receive part of the benefits.

And in 1989-90, when there was an epidemic of crack babies in Atlanta, too many for Grady to handle, their collaborative effort shared in taking care of the patients. (The impetus came from the urging of pediatrician Marty Moran, an active member of the Medical Association of Atlanta and of the Scottish Rite and Northside staffs.)

APPENDIX TEN
Yes, Virginia, There Really is a Sandy Spring
(A Thumbnail History)

White men first coming into the area in the 1820s found the Creek Indians camping around fresh water bubbling up through sand. Later the spring was a watering stop for Atlanta-bound travelers and their horses.

In 1821 the Creek Indians yielded to the U.S. government an area which was divided into five counties. Each district was nine miles square and each land lot was 45 chain lengths square, or 202 1/2 acres. (The surveyor's chain length was 66 feet; the chain was made up of 100 chain links, each 7.9 inches long.) Land in the community was originally distributed by lottery.

Sandy Springs was originally part of DeKalb County, which was created in 1822. Fulton County was subsequently formed out of DeKalb, and in 1853 Sandy Springs was included in Fulton County. A spring house has been restored over the original springs, located off Sandy Springs Circle, by the 24Sandy Springs Historic Community Foundation. The foundation was chartered in 1985 after the community was incensed by a request before the Fulton County Commission in 1985 to rezone the property so that the springs could be covered with fill dirt and a shopping center built over it. Working with members of the Sandy Springs Garden Club, the foundation also acquired the Williams-Payne farmhouse, one of the few houses built before 1900 still around, and placed it next to the springs. The restored house is now a museum depicting life in Sandy Springs between 1870 and 1900 and is open for public tour. The Historic Site is owned by Fulton County and is operated by the foundation in conjunction with Fulton County Department of Parks and Recreation.

(Abridged from *Sandy Springs — Past Tense*, Lois Coogle. Sandy Springs Historic Community Foundation, Inc. 1991.)

APPENDIX ELEVEN
The Georgia Hospital-Medical Council

In 1963 my committee assignment in the Georgia Radiological Society was to represent it on the Georgia Hospital-Medical Council (GHMC), which I had scarcely heard of. It was a refreshing surprise — and an education.

It had been formed five years before as a joint program of 14 of Georgia's voluntary medical and health organizations (Georgia Academy of General Practice, American College of Surgeons, Georgia Association of Hospital Governing Boards, Georgia Association of Pathologists, American College of Hospital Administrators, Georgia Department of Family and Children Services, Georgia Department of Public Health, Georgia Hospital Association, Georgia Radiological Society, Georgia Society of Anesthesiologists, Georgia Society of Internal Medicine, Georgia State OB-Gyn Society, Medical Association of Georgia and Georgia Nursing Home Association).

It received national attention with this unique program — the first of its type in the country to promote higher standards of patient care. Its program included three principal activities: (1) conducting a formal accreditation service for hospitals under 25 beds in size (at that time there were a number of these, ineligible to apply for an inspection by the national Joint Commission on Accreditation of Hospitals; (2) inspecting and recommending hospitals over 25 beds in size (and not accredited by the national Joint Commission) to the State Department of Family and Children Services for participation in the Old Age Assistance medical care program. In 1963 hospital administrators and physicians throughout the state contributed their time and travel to carry out 70 hospital inspections (and in 1964 it produced a standards and accreditation program for nursing homes). The representatives of these organizations worked so well together that the GHMC decided to (3) provide a consultation service to hospitals, when requested, in the matter of medical staff-administration-governing board relationships. The first joint request, in 1963, was by the Georgia Hospital Association, the Medical Association of Georgia and the Georgia Association of Hospital Governing Boards because of conflicts between hospitals and radiologists in some smaller towns. In one instance the hospital had fired the radiologist because he had refused to accept a new percentage contract (radiologists in those days did not render bills separate from the hospitals) which was lower than he had worked under previously. In another instance, a radiologist was being threatened with the same fate. And other issues were reported.

In April 1963 the GHMC appointed a six-member committee to conduct a thorough study of relationships between radiologists and hospitals with the ultimate purpose of recommending guidelines for hospitals and radiologists in their contractual and professional relationship. The committee reviewed and evaluated the principles currently accepted by national and state hospital and radiological organizations, obtained legal counsel from two sources, sent questionnaires to all radiologists, hospital governing boards, and chiefs of the medical staff of each of the hospitals on the mailing list of the Georgia Hospital Association, and invited hospital governing boards and radiologists involved in dispute to present their views. Forty-six radiologists responded in detail about their contracts with 70 hospitals and over 70 replies were sent by governing boards and medical staff chiefs.

Over 11 months the committee held numerous sessions and hammered out a set of guidelines and recommendations which were approved by the entire membership of the GHMC and published in booklet form. The guide was quite useful, but became obsolete in 1966-68, when, at the urging of the American College of Radiology, radiologists switched from percentage contracts (with the hospital presenting a single bill to the patient) to rendering separate bills for their services. The GHMC also became obsolete and disappeared before the time Northside opened.